THE LIEUTENANT AND OTHERS

THE LIEUTENANT AND OTHERS

BY

"SAPPER"

AUTHOR OF "SERGEANT MICHAEL CASSIDY, R.E."

HODDER AND STOUGHTON
LONDON   NEW YORK   TORONTO
MCMXVI

Printed in Great Britain by Hazell, Watson & Viney, Ld.,
London and Aylesbury.

PREFACE

It is perhaps unnecessary to state that none of the sketches in this book refer to any particular individual. They are not arranged in chronological order ; they do not pretend to be anything more than mere impressions of the grim drama now being played across the water.

Some of those pictured in these pages have gone across the Vale of Shadows : may the earth lie lightly on them, one and all. Others there are who, perchance, may think they recognise themselves here and there : to them I dedicate the book.

The setting in most of the sketches is the salient of Ypres : there may be some who will recognise—not, I trust, without a throb of pleasure—Hooge, Frizenburg, the Menin-gate, and other health resorts of that delectable neighbourhood.

But should I lift in the smallest degree, for those who wait behind, the curtain that shrouds " somewhere in France," and show them the tears and the laughter, the humour and the pathos that go to form the atmosphere over yonder, I shall be well satisfied.

I am no artist in words, but—" Each in his separate star shall paint the thing as he sees it for the God of things as they are."

CONTENTS

THE LIEUTENANT

A FORTNIGHT IN FRANCE
MAY 10 TO MAY 24, 1915

I

GERALD AINSWORTH was the only son of his parents—and they made something in tins. He had lots of money, as the sons of people who dabble in tins frequently do. He was a prominent member of several dull night-clubs, where he was in the habit of seeing life while other people saw his money. He did nothing and was generally rather bored with the process. In fact, he was a typical product of the twentieth century—with his father's house in the country full of footmen and ancestors, both types guaranteed by the best references—and his own rooms in London full of clothes and photographs. He was a very fair sample of that dread disease, "the Nut," and it was not altogether his own fault. Given an income that enabled him to do what he liked, certain that he would never be called on to work for his living, he

I

had degenerated into a drifter through the pleasant paths of life—a man who had never done one single thing of the very slightest use to himself or anybody else. Then came the war, and our hero, who was not by any means a bad fellow at heart, obtained a commission. It was a bit of an event in the family of Ainsworth—*née* Blobbs—and the soldier-ancestor of Charles I.'s reign smiled approval from the walls of the family dining-room: as I have said, it was guaranteed to behave as all well-brought-up ancestors are reputed to do.

Gerald was becomingly modest about it all, and, to do him credit, did not suffer from uniformitis as badly as some I wot of. It is possible that a small episode which occurred in the drawing-room of the baronial hall had something to do with it—for, I will repeat, he was not a bad fellow at heart. And this was the episode.

.   .   .   .

Coming in one Saturday afternoon on week-end leave in the full glory of his new uniform, he found the room full of girls—his income would in time be over five figures, his return for the week-end had not been kept secret,

and there may or may not be a connection.
Also there were his mother and father and
one very bored man of about thirty in plain
clothes.

" This is my son, Gerald," cooed the old
lady. " So splendid of him, you know, joining the Army. This dreadful war, you know.
More tea, my dear. Poor things, out there
—how I pity them. Quite terrible. But
don't you think it's splendid, the way they're
all joining ? "

The bored man in mufti looked more bored.
" Why ? " he asked resignedly.

" Why ! " echoed a creation on his right
indignantly. " How can you ask such a
thing ? Think of all the hardship and suffering they'll have to endure. Isn't that
enough ? " and she glanced tenderly at Gerald,
while six other creations bit savagely at
muffins because she'd got it out first.

" I don't quite follow the argument,"
answered the bored man patiently. " If a
man has no ties, I don't see that there is any
credit in his joining the Army. It is his plain
duty, and the gravest discredit attaches to
him if he doesn't. Don't you agree with
me ? " and he turned to Gerald.

"Certainly," answered Gerald, with the faintest hesitation. The line of argument was a little new.

"And what regiment are *you* going to join?" remarked another creation, with dangerous sweetness.

The bored man smiled slightly. "The one I've been in for ten years. I've just come back from Central Africa and cross the day after to-morrow."

As I have said, it is possible that this small incident tended to make the disease of uniformitis a mild one in our hero's case, and to bring home to him exactly what the pukka soldier does think of it all.

Time went on as time will do, and over his doings in the winter I will not linger. Bar the fact that he'd been worked till he was just about as fit as a man can be, I really know nothing about them. My story is of his coming to France and what happened to him while he was there till, stopping one in the shoulder, he went back to England feet first—a man, where before he had been an ass. He was only in France a fortnight, from the time he landed at Havre till the time they put him on a hospital ship at Boulogne;

but in that fortnight he lived and, not to put too fine a point on it, deuced nearly died as well ; so he got his money's worth.

. . . . .

And now, for I have lingered too much on the introduction of my hero, I will get to business.

. . . . .

The train crept on through the night—now pulling up with a series of nerve-shattering jolts, then on again at its apparently maximum speed of twenty miles an hour. In the corner of a so-called first-class carriage Gerald Ainsworth stared into the darkness with unseeing eyes. The dim shapes that flashed past him seemed like the phantasmagoria of a dream. For the first time for three days he had the time to think. He recalled the lunch in Southampton when he had said good-bye to various people who seemed to have a slight difficulty in speaking. He remembered dining in the hotel whose sacred portals are barred to the civilian, still in ignorance of where he was going—to France, the Dardanelles, or even farther afield. Then all the bustle of embarking the regiment and, later, disembarking. And now he was actually under way, starting on the Great Adventure. There were others in the carriage with him, but only one was asleep and he did not belong to the regiment. To him the Adventure had ceased to be great ; it was old and stale, and he had spent most of his time cursing at not being able to raise a motor-car. For when you know the ropes —be it whispered—it is generally your own fault if you travel by supply train. But of that the man who sat staring out of the window knew nothing. All he knew was that every minute carried him nearer the unknown—the unknown of which he had read so much and knew so little.

His equipment was very new and beautiful —and very bulky. Prominent among it was that abomination of desolation the fitted mess-tin. Inside it reposed little receptacles for salt and pepper and plates and dinner napkins and spirit lamps that explode like bombs. Aunts are aunts, and there was none to tell him that the roads of Flanders are paved with fitted mess-tins. His revolver was loaded—in fact, five of those dangerous weapons reposed in the racks. The gentle-

long-pointed bayonet at the crossing just outside the station seemed the only thing alive besides himself and his men. The man opposite, who had slept so soundly, had disappeared, swearing volubly, to lie in wait for a motor-car. And then happening to look at the colonel he found him in earnest consultation with an officer, who sported a red band on his arm. This extremely crusty individual he subsequently discovered boasted the mystic letters R. T. O. on his band— which for the benefit of the uninitiated may be translated Railway Transport Officer And though as a rule their duties do not carry them within range of the festive obus, or shell, yet their crustiness—the few who are crusty—may be forgiven them. For to them come wandering at all hours of the twenty-four men of all sorts, sizes, and descriptions, bleating for information and help. The type of individual who has lost his warrant, his equipment, and his head, and doesn't know where he is bound for, but it is somewhere beginning with a B, is particularly popular with them early in the morning. However, that is all by the way.

.   .   .   .   .

They filed out of the station and the battalion sat down beside the road, while the cooks got busy over breakfast. Periodically a Staff officer hacked by on a rustic morning liver-shaker, and a couple of aeroplanes, flying low, passed over their heads bound on an early reconnaissance. They were still many miles from the firing line and, save for a low but insistent muttering, coming sullenly through the still morning air, they might have been in England. In fact, it was a great deal more peaceful than training in England. The inhabitants passing by scarcely turned their heads to look at them —and, save for the inevitable crowd of small children who alternately sucked their dirty thumbs and demanded, " Cigarette, souvenir," no one seemed at all interested in their existence. Everything was very different from the tin-god atmosphere of England.

At last a whistle blew and there was a general tightening of belts and straps. The battalion fell in, and with its head to the east swung off along the dusty road towards the distant muttering guns. As a route march it was much like other route marches—except

that they were actually in Flanders. The
country was flat and uninteresting. The
roads were *pavé* and very unpleasant to
march on. Ainsworth's pack felt con-
foundedly heavy, and the top had come off
the pepper receptacle in the fitted mess-tin.
They passed some Indians squatting in a
field by the roadside, and occasionally a
party of cavalry horses out on exercise—for
the cavalry were up in the trenches, and when
they're up there they leave the horses behind.
Also gilded beings in motor-cars went past
periodically, to the accompaniment of curses
and much dust. The battalion was singing
as it swung along, and in front a band of a
sort gave forth martial music—the principal
result of which was to bring those auditors
not connected with the regiment cursing
from their bivouacs at the unseemly noise.

.   .   .   .   .

And then miles away in the distance they
saw a line of little white puffs up in the blue
of the sky—a new one appearing every second.
It was Archibald—or the anti-aircraft gun—
" doing the dirty," that fruitful source of stiff
necks to those who see him for the first time.
But I will not dwell on that route march.

It was, as I have said, much like others, only more so. That evening a very hot, tired, and dusty battalion came to rest in some wooden huts beside the road—their home for the next two or three days. The guns were much louder now, though everything else was still very quiet. Away about four or five miles in front of them a great pall of smoke hung lazily in the air—marking the funeral pyre of ill-fated " Wipers." For that was their destination in the near future, as Ainsworth had already found out from the adjutant.

Opposite them, on the other side of the road, a cavalry regiment just out of the trenches was resting. Everything seemed perfectly normal—no one seemed to feel the slightest excitement at being within half a dozen miles of the firing line. The officers over the way were ragging—much as they did at home. After a cursory glance at his battalion, to size it up, none of them had paid the slightest attention to them. The arrival of some new men was too common a sight for anyone to get excited about—but Ainsworth could not be expected to know that.

He had strolled out just before dinner,

and as he reached a bend in the road the evening frightfulness in Ypres started. For ten minutes or a quarter of an hour a furious shelling went on, gradually dying away to comparative quiet again.

" Is anything happening ? " he asked of a passing cavalry subaltern.

" Not that I know of," returned the other in some surprise.

" But they're shelling very hard, aren't they ? "

" That ! That's nothing—they do that most nights. Are you just out ? Where are you going ? "

" Wipers, I think. What's it like ? "

" Damnable," rejoined the other tersely, and with that the conversation languished.

For all that, when Gerald pulled the blankets up to his chin that night the feeling in the pit of his stomach had gone. He felt that he'd started to bat—that he was actually in the dentist's chair.

.　　.　　.　　.　　.

Three days of complete quiet passed— three days that seemed to give the lie to his laconic cavalry acquaintance. Occasionally a burst of shelling proclaimed that neither

side was actually asleep, and at night, towards
the south, the green German flares could be
seen like brilliant stars in the sky. In the
main, however, peace was the order of the
day. Those who knew were not deceived,
however, for there were many lulls before
the storm in the second battle of Ypres
—that long-drawn-out struggle round the
salient. But to the battalion—just arrived—
the whole thing seemed rather disappoint-
ing. They were tired of Archies and
aeroplanes : they were tired of the red glow
they could see through the trees at night—
where Ypres lay burning ; above all, they
were tired of getting smothered with dust
from passing motor-lorries and ambulances
which crashed up and down the road at all
hours of the day and night. Like everyone
when they first arrived, they wanted to be up
and at it. The men had all been issued with
respirators, and nightly did breathing exer-
cises—in through the mouth and out through
the nose—to the accompaniment of facetious
remarks from the onlookers. They had not
dabbled in Hun gas as yet, nor appreciated
its delights, so the parade was not a popular
one. Comments on " 'Im with the Iron

Mask," and requests of a personal nature to your friends always to wear a pad owing to their improved appearance, enlivened what otherwise would have been a somewhat boring performance. A week later—but I will not anticipate.

Ainsworth himself, to pass the time, had tried a little bomb-throwing with his platoon. This also had not been an unqualified success. As far as the jam tins and hand grenades were concerned, everything in the garden was lovely. Quite a number went off, and all would have been well had not the tempter tempted. Reposing on the ground—brought up by an imbecile sergeant—lay a rifle grenade, that infernal invention which, on leaving the rifle, puts a boomerang to shame and generally winds up in the commanding officer's dug-out, there exploding with great force. However, as I have remarked before, Ainsworth could not be expected to know that. Knowledge on the avoidance of supply trains, and boredom, and the devilry that lies latent in a rifle grenade comes only with many weary weeks. So he fired it. Away it went, soaring into space, and at length a great explosion announced that all was over.

2

"It seemed to go some way, sir," said the sergeant.

"It did," answered Ainsworth, "farther than I thought." His face expressed a little uneasiness, when suddenly an apparition appeared. Hopping over a ploughed field towards him, brandishing his arms, came an infuriated figure in carpet slippers. The platoon paused in silent dismay, while a bull-like bellow came floating through the air.

"You blithering ass," roared an excited voice, as a purple-faced gunner-major came to a standstill in front of him. "You fat-headed, splay-footed idiot. I have been shelled and gassed and shot at for two months without a pause by the Germans, and when I come back here to rest you plaster my picket line with lumps of steel, and burst lyddite bombs on my bed!"

"I'm very sorry, sir," said Ainsworth. "I'd no idea——"

"Then, damn it, go away and get one. Go away and make noises and explosions in your own bed, or apply to go to the Dardanelles, or something. You're a menace, sir, a pest, and you ought to be locked up."

So that, all things being considered, it came
as a distinct relief to our somewhat ruffed
and misunderstood hero when, on returning
to lunch, he found the battalion was going up
into the reserve trenches that night.

III

AND so it came to pass that at six o'clock
that evening Gerald Ainsworth, with a few
other officers of his battalion, jogged slowly
along in a bone-shaking wagon toward Ypres.
He was going up early to take over the
trenches from the battalion they were re-
lieving, which in turn was going up to the
front line. Past the station with its twisted
rails and splintered sleepers, past the water-
tower, almost untouched at that time amid
the general devastation, on down the road,
and then right-handed into the square. Some
blackened half-burned carcases lying under
the ruins of the Cloth Hall—the first actual
trace of war he had seen—held him fascinated.
Down a side street a house was burning
fiercely, but of life there was none, except
one military policeman watching for looters.

A very young subaltern on the box-seat was being entertained by the A.S.C. driver—one of the good old sort. Six officers fresh from home—thirsting for blood—should they not have it ? Every shell-hole held a story, and the driver was an artist. " You can take it from me, sir, and I knows. This 'ere place weren't no blooming picnic three weeks ago. The major, he says to me, ' Jones,' he says, ' the ration limbers have gone off and have forgotten the tea. I looks to you to get the tea to them lads in the trenches. Also, there's an allowance of pepper been sent out in a parcel by the League of Beauty in Tooting for our gallant defenders in France —put that in too.'

" ' Very good, sir.' I says. ' They shall have their tea and their pepper, or my name's not Alf Jones.'

" With that, sir, I harnesses up the old horses and I gallops. Through 'ere I comes, the old horses going like two-year-olds. And then they was shelling it, no blooming error. As I was going through, the cathedral fell down and one of the tiles hit me on the napper. But what did I care ? Just as I gets here I meets a party of officers—three generals and their Staff blokes. Says they to me, they says, ' Stop, for the generals are gassed and you must take us away.'

" I says to 'em, I says, ' And what about the pepper, gentlemen, for the men in the trenches ? '

" ' Pepper ! ' cries a Staff officer, and as he spoke we took it, sir. Right into the back of the wagon they put a seventeen-inch shell, and the gift from the League of Beauty was all over the square. Sneeze !—you should have 'eard us. The Commander-in-Chief— 'e sneezed the gas right out of 'im, and the Linseed Lancer 'e says to me, 'e says, ' Jones, you've saved our lives.'

" ' Yus,' I says, ' you're welcome to any little thing like that ; but what about them poor trusting girls and their pepper ? ' "

It was at this moment, I subsequently gathered, that my subaltern hove in sight carrying two large mirrors under his arm and, finding where they were going, demanded a lift.

" Very quiet to-night," he remarked, when he was stowed inside. " I've just been looting mirrors for periscopes."

.   .   .   .   .   .

Now, I've brought him into the story, because he was the first man to tell them that the reserve trenches they were occupying were not all honey and strawberry jam. He's a useless young blighter, and unless he's watched very carefully he always drinks more than his fair share of port. But, in view of the fact that other people will arrive in time and go and sit—if not in those particular trenches, at any rate in trenches like them— I would like to point out that the man on the spot knows what he's talking about. Also that, because for three days on end you do a thing with perfect safety, it does not follow that you won't be killed doing it the fourth. And I would like it to be clearly established that my port-drinking looter of mirrors told the officers in the wagon that the line they were going into was habitually shelled. Remember, everything was quiet. Those who may happen to read these words and who know Ypres will bear me witness as to how quiet it can be, and will agree with me that it can frequently be—otherwise.

Now, they dropped him half way, at a place where there are cellars in which a man may live in safety, and there they disembarked

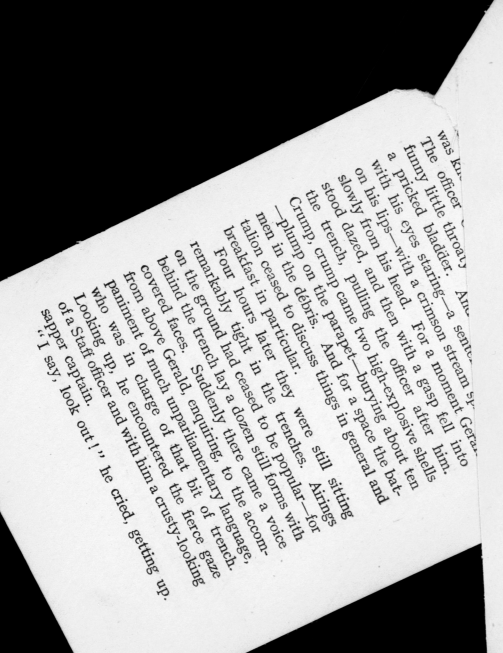

was kn...

The officer ... An...
funny little throat ...
a pricked bladder. For a moment Gera...
with his eyes staring—a crimson stream ...
on his lips—with a gasp ... after him.
slowly from his head. And then with ... ten
stood dazed, and then the officer ... about the bat-
the trench, pulling the officer—burying
Crump, crump came two high-explosive shells
—plump on the parapet—for a space the bat-
men in the débris. And for a space in general and
talion in particular. were still sitting
breakfast in the trenches. Airings
Four hours later they to be popular—for
remarkably tight in the trenches with
on the ground had ceased to be popular still forms with
behind the trench lay a dozen came a voice
covered faces. Suddenly there ...tary language,
from above Gerald, enquiring, to the accompaniment of much unparliamentary ... the fierce gaze
who was in charge of that bit of trench.
Looking up, he encountered the fierce ...looking
of a Staff officer and with him a crusty-looking
sapper captain.

"I say, look out!" he cried, getting up.

from the wagon and walked : and all was
peace. One dead horse—a very dead horse
—raised its voice to heaven in mute protest ;
but otherwise all was perfectly peaceful.
Two or three shells passed overhead as they
walked down the road, but these were quite
obviously harmless. And suddenly one of
our own batteries let drive from close by
with a deafening bang. Nothing untoward
occurred, and yet they were quite near
enough to hear individual rifle shots.

. . . . .

And so they came to the trenches which
they were to occupy, and found them full
of a regiment which had been in them for
two days and was going up to the front line
that night. The right flank rested on a railway
line and the left on no special mark in particular. Away in front of them on the left
a dull brownish smudge could be seen on
the ground—in a place where the country
was open. The German trenches ! Who does
not remember the feelings with which he
first contemplated the German front trench
and realised that there actually reposed the
Huns ? And, in passing, it's a strange fact,
but nevertheless a true one, that quite a

number of men have been out to the tren...
survived two or three days, been wou...
and gone home without so much as se...
Boche.

That night the battalion made t...
acquaintance with trenches as a bed...
they were dry, as trenches go, th...
suffered, in common with all oth...
from an eruption of small po...
occurring exactly where you...
your head. And now the ti...
me to justify my subaltern...
entry into this story. As I...
warned that party of offi...
was not healthy at all...
was as the voice of the...
ever it was who c...
rning—a b...
ke up...

" It's awful up there. We lost about thirty
men this morning."

" So I see," answered the Staff officer.
" What the deuce were they doing up here ?
Are you aware that this is under direct
observation from the Germans ? Some of
you fellows seem to think that because
things are quiet for five minutes you can
dance pastoral dances in front of your
trenches." He grunted dispassionately.

. . . . .

The sapper captain took up the ball.
" What do you propose to do where the
parapet has collapsed ? " he enquired.

" I really hadn't thought about it," answered Ainsworth, looking at the collapsed
trench. " I haven't had any orders."

" Orders ! On matters of that sort you
don't receive them ; you give them. On the
road are hundreds of sandbags, thousands of
sandbags, millions of——" The Staff officer
caught his eye. Daily they quarrelled over
sandbags. " At any rate," he went on firmly,
" there are lots of sandbags. Go and get
them. Fill them. Build up the bally trench,
and don't leave it like that for the next poor
blighters. Work on trenches is never finished.

You can go on for days and weeks and months——" But the Staff officer was leading him away. " Years, I tell you, can you work on these d—— trenches: and he waits for orders ! "

" Peter, you're feverish." The Staff officer gently drew him on and they suddenly paused. " What," he cried, in a voice of concentrated fury, gazing at a trench full of faces upturned to the sky, " what are you looking at ? Turn your faces down, you fat-headed dolts. I know it's a German aeroplane—I saw it three minutes ago—and there you sit with a row of white faces gazing up at him, so as to leave him in no doubt that the trenches are occupied. Keep down and don't move, and above all don't show him a great line of white blotches. They're bad enough for us to bear as it is, but——"

" James, you're feverish now." It was the sapper officer's turn to draw him away. " But I admit," he remarked sadly as they faded away, " that it's all quite dreadful. They learn in time, but, to begin with, they want nurses."

And, lest the morning perambulation of these two weary officers may seem inconsistent in any way with their words, I would point out that what two or three may do in perfect safety a body of men may not. They don't as a rule waste shells on an isolated man in khaki, and these particular trenches were out of rifle range.

For the time, therefore, we will leave Gerald building up his trench with those twelve silent bodies behind—eloquent testimony that appearances are deceitful and that the man on the spot knows best.

IV

" Is that the guide ? What, you're the general's cook ! Well, where the devil is the guide ? All right, lead on." The battalion was moving up into the front line trenches, after two uneventful days in reserve. Their lesson well learnt, they had kept under cover, and the only diversion had been the sudden appearance out of heaven of an enormous piece of steel which had descended from the skies with great rapidity and an unpleasant zogging sort of noise. The mystery was unearthed from the parapet where it had embedded itself, and completely defeated everyone; till a stray gunner, passing, told them that it was merely part of a German Archie shell—which had burst up at a great height and literally fallen like manna from the heavens.

"Slow in front — for Heaven's sake." Agitated mutterings from the rear came bursting up to the front of the column, mingled with crashes and stifled oaths as men fell into shell-holes they couldn't see, probably half-full of water.

"Keep still—duck." An insistent order muttered from every officer as a great green flare shot up into the night and, falling on the ground near them, burnt fiercely and then went out, leaving everything blacker than ever. On their left a working party furiously deepened a communication trench that already resembled a young river. Coming on their right, as they crept and stumbled along in single file, a small party of men loomed out of the night. More agitated mutterings: "Who are you?" and from a medley of answers, comprising everyone from the Archbishop of Canterbury to the Kaiser, the fact emerges that they are the ration party of the regiment on their right.

. . . . .

At last a halt. The head of the battalion has reached the trenches and the men begin getting in. Not used to the game, there is a lot of unnecessary delay before the men are settled and the other regiment away. They have left behind two or three officers to introduce the new men to the trenches, explain exactly what places are healthy and what are not—where the ammunition is kept, and the bombs, and the flares.

" A sniper with a fixed rifle has the other side of this traverse marked," said one of the officers to Gerald. " He's up in a tree somewhere—so don't keep any men on the other side of it. He's killed a lot of ours. Listen to him." And from the other side came a ping—thud, as the bullet hit the earth. Merely a rifle set on a certain mark during the day, and loosed off ten or eleven times every hour during the night—hoping to bag something.

" They're pretty quiet here at present," he was told, " but I don't trust 'em a yard. They're too quiet. Bavarians. If you want to, there's an officer out in front about fifty yards away with a good helmet on. Thought of going out myself last night—but they were too bally busy with their flares. Still —the helmet's worth getting. Well, so long, I think I've shown you everything. Bye-bye. Oh! while I think of it, they've got a bit of this communication trench, about forty yards down, marked. I'd get it deepened."

And with that he went, and Ainsworth was alone. Stray rifle shots cracking through the night—flares going up with steady persistency. He tested his telephone to Head-quarters—it was working. He went along his length of trench—one man watching in each little length, the rest lying down with rifles by their sides. Occasionally the watching man gave them one round to show the Hun he wasn't forgotten; while without intermission the ping—thud from the fixed rifle came into the earth of the traverse. It formed a sort of lullaby to Gerald. The awakening was drastic.

. . . . .

Just as the dawn was faintly streaking the sky, and the men all awake were gripping their rifles in anticipation of any possible attack, the first shells burst along the line. From then on, for what seemed an eternity and was in reality two hours, the shells poured in without cessation. Shrapnel, high explosive, and sometimes a great sausage-shaped fellow, came twisting and hurtling through the air, exploding, with a most deafening roar. That was the *Minenwerfer* (trench howitzer). The fumes from the shells got into their eyes, the parapet collapsed, traverses broke down, men gasping, twisting, buried. And still they came. Men, those who still lived, lay dazed and helpless. Whole sections of the front of the trench were torn away in great craters. In some places men, their reason almost gone, got blindly out of the trench—their one idea to get away from the ghastly living death. But if death was probable in the trench, it was certain outside. The deadly rain of shrapnel searched them out, and one by one they fell. Some, perhaps, dragged on a space with shattered legs, muttering and moaning till another tearing explosion gave them peace.

" Keep down, keep down ! " Ainsworth tried to shout. His lips, trembling with the fearful nerve-shattering inferno, could hardly frame the words. When they came it was only a whisper, but had he shouted through a megaphone none would have heard. The din was too incredible.

And still they came. His eyes were fixed stupidly on a man kneeling down behind a traverse, who was muttering foolishly to himself. He saw his lips moving, he cursed him foolishly, childishly, when, with a roar that seemed to split his whole head open, a high-explosive shell burst on the traverse itself. The man who had been muttering fell forward, was hurled forward, and his head stuck out of the earth which had fallen on him. Gerald laughed. It was deuced funny; he started to howl with mirth, when suddenly the head rolled towards him. But he could not stop laughing.

.   .   .   .   .

At last he pulled himself together. So this was what he had read about so often in the papers at home, was it?—" a furious bombardment of our trenches." Perhaps, though, he reflected, this was not a furious bombardment; perhaps this was only " a slight artillery activity upon our front." And then

3

he very nearly started laughing again. It was all so frightfully funny ; the actual thing was so utterly different. And so far he had not seen a German. Everything had been so completely peaceful—until that morning —and then, without warning—this. Most amazing of all, he was not touched, and as that realisation first took hold of him so his dulled faculties first grasped the fact that the fire was slackening. It was, and, just like a tropical storm, suddenly it seemed to die away. Shells still passed screaming overhead, but those devastating explosions on the trenches—on his trenches—had ceased. Like the sudden cessation of bad toothache, he could hardly believe it at first. His mind, his brain were still dazed ; he seemed to be waking from a nightmare, but only half-awake. How long he lay there no one will ever know, trying to steady his hand, to still the twitching of his muscles ; but suddenly he was recalled to his senses by seeing a figure coming crawling round the shattered traverse. It was his captain.

" Thank Heaven, you've not stopped one, old boy ! " he said. " Good God ! You've had it bad here."

Gerald nodded ; he could not speak. His captain looked at him and so did the sapper officer who came behind ; and, being men of understanding, for a space there was silence.

" Worst bit of the whole line," said the sapper. " We must hold it where we can to-day and get it patched up to-night."

" How many men have you got left, Gerald, in your platoon ? "

" I don't know," he answered, and his voice sounded strange. He looked to see if the others noticed it, but they made no sign. As a matter of fact, his voice was quavering like an old man's—but, as I have said, they were men of understanding. " I'll go and see."

And so the three crawled on, and in various odd corners they pulled out white-faced men. One in a corner was mad. He was playing a game by himself with another man's boot— a boot that contained its original owner's foot. One man was sobbing quietly, but most of them were just staring dazedly in front of them.

.   .   .   .   .

Suddenly Gerald clutched his captain's arm.

" Heavens ! sir," he croaked, " they can get through here."

" Not by day," answered the sapper. " The ground in front is enfiladed from higher up, and, as a matter of fact, they show no signs of advancing. The bombardment has failed."

" Failed ! Failed ! " croaked Ainsworth, and he laughed hideously. " Rather—I noticed the failure."

" Nevertheless, old chap, what I say is right. They've failed because they can't advance." He put his hand on Gerald's arm for a moment. " They may try to make a small local advance to-night under cover of dark, but I don't think we'll be troubled till then. They won't renew the bombardment, from what I know of 'em." And with that he was gone.

And so Gerald gathered together the remnants of his platoon, and there were fifteen all told. He put them where he could and waited for the night, when, with another working party, the trenches could be built up to their proper shape again. And then he went and sat down again and wondered at life. Overhead the shells still screamed

on their way. In the distance the dull boom
of their explosion still came reverberating
through the air.

He was getting fairly skilled now in estimat-
ing where they would burst, for a desultory
shelling of the trenches was still going on,
though not in his section of the line. And
it was then that I think the ass period
emerged from the chrysalis stage and the man
appeared. For as he listened to the rushing
noise through the air, saw the great cloud of
blackish white smoke, and later heard the
roar of the explosion somewhere down the
line, it was borne in on him that there were
other things in the world besides night clubs,
that there were other things besides cocktails
and whisky sours and amusing women, and
that a new force was at work—the force of
Death—which made them all seem very
petty. The ancestors seemed a bit petty,
the money that came from things in tins
seemed a bit petty; he only remembered
a head rolling towards him with gaping
mouth and staring eyes. It struck him that
his might have been the head.

V

Now, in reading over what I have written concerning the commencement of Gerald Ainsworth's pilgrimage in the smiling fields of Flanders, I feel that I too have merited the rebuke so quietly given him in those words, "They have failed." He had lost his sense of proportion—about which another and a worthier pen than mine has written in connection with this same game of war—and I too have perhaps given those who may read these pages an unfair impression.

That bombardment of which I have told was not an ordinary one, it is true, but at the same time it was not anything very extraordinary. Considered by the men who occupied those trenches, it was the nearest approach to a complete cataclysm of the universe that can be conceived of; considered by the men who sit behind and move the pawns on the board, it was a furious bombardment of one five-hundredth of what they were responsible for. Moreover, it had failed. But it is not to be wondered at that when, some time later, Gerald was attempting to give his father some impression of what that morning had been like that worthy old gentleman should have expressed great surprise and indignation that it was not reported in the papers, and stated with some freedom his opinion on the muzzling of the English Press. And yet, would it not have been making a mountain out of a mole-hill—a great battle out of nothing at all? Yes, nothing at all; for in this struggle what are fifty, a hundred men—provided the enemy does not get what it wants? Much to the relatives of the fifty, but nothing to the result. Hard, but true. A somewhat bitter fact. However, all this is a digression.

We left Gerald, I think, with the remnants of his platoon scattered along what once were trenches, holding them till under cover of night a fresh working party could come up and rebuild them. The wire in front of him had been destroyed by the shell fire, and nothing but a piece of field, pitted and torn up by explosions, separated him from the Germans fifty yards away. The Germans facing him had established a superiority of rifle fire. Secure in practically undamaged trenches, did a man but show his hat opposite them it was riddled with bullets.

Wherefore, after a couple of the remnants of the platoon had ill-advisedly shown their hats with their heads inside them, and a second later had subsided with a choking grunt and a final kick, the survivors confined their attention to the bottom of the trench, and from it sorted out the bombs and the flares and the reserve ammunition. Also they sorted out other things, which we need not specify, and threw them out behind, where in time perhaps they might be decently buried. And then, having done all they could, they sat down with their backs to the parapet and hoped for the best. It was not till half-past eight that night that the German artillery condescended to notice them again, and then for about ten minutes they put a desultory fire of shrapnel on to the trenches. Then the range lengthened.

.   .   .   .   .

Now Gerald was no fool, and suddenly the words of the sapper captain in the morning rang through his brain. "They may make a small local advance under cover of dark." It was almost dark : they had shelled the trenches—apparently aimlessly—and now were shooting behind on the support trenches. Why ? He grovelled in the bottom of the trench and found a Very pistol and flare. Up it shot into the air, and as it did he saw them—the whole line saw them—and the fun started. The mad minute started in earnest all along the trench. The trench that enfiladed the ground in front of him got going with a Maxim, flares flew up into the air from all along the line, falling behind the advancing Germans. For about ten minutes the most glorious pandemonium reigned : everyone was mixed up endways. In places the English had come out of their trenches and were going for them grunting and snarling in the open with bayonets. In places they were fighting in our trenches—in places we were in theirs. The Maxim had ceased for fear of hitting its own men, and without intermission flares went up from both sides. Suddenly, on top of Gerald as he stood blazing away into the dusk, there loomed a Bavarian officer. It was touch and go, and if a sergeant beside him had shot a second later this yarn might have had to close here. As it was, the bullet from the

Bavarian officer's revolver found a home in the earth, and the Bavarian himself fell with a crash to the bottom of the trench.

But it could not go on. In places they were breaking ; in places they were broken ; but, unfortunately, in one place they had got through. At the extreme left of Gerald's trench, which he had been unable to reach during the day owing to a huge hole blown out of the parapet, the Germans had scrambled in. Elsewhere they had fallen back to their own lines, pursued the whole way by men stabbing and hacking at them, their eyes red with the lust of killing, getting a bit of their own back after the unspeakable hell of the morning. And what but a quarter of an hour previously had been bare, open ground was now covered with motionless bodies, from which, later, a few wounded would drag themselves back to their own people.

.   .   .   .   .

It was when comparative quiet again reigned that one of his sergeants came to Gerald and reported the uninvited appearance of the Germans away down on the left. Now the presence of the enemy in your own trench in small parties is, I understand, a thing that has frequently puzzled those who read about it at home. It is, however, a thing of fairly common occurrence, and a small hostile party on the offensive may prove extremely unpleasant. The whole thing becomes a question of bombs and rapidity of action. Also, I will willingly lay two to one on the side that gets off the mark first. A traverse, as everyone knows, is a great lump of the original soil left standing when the trench is dug, and round which the trench is cut. Its object is to localise the bursts of high-explosive shell. As you cannot see round a corner or through solid earth, it is, therefore, obvious that you cannot see from one bit of fire trench into the next, though you can get there by walking round the traverse. If, however, there is a man sitting waiting for you with a rifle this process is not to be recommended, as he will certainly get in the first shot at a range of about five yards.

Now all that Gerald knew, and, to his credit be it said, he acted with promptitude and without hesitation, and the man who does that in war, as in other things, generally acts with success.

" Bombs ! " he cried to the sergeant who had told him. " Bombs of all sorts—plum and apple, hair-brush, any damn thing you can get, and all the men at once ! " They scrabbled them out of the débris and searched for them in the mud, where they had been buried, and at last the party was ready—ten in all.

" What's the jest ? " said the sapper officer, dropping into the trench as they were being mustered.

" Boches lower down. We're bombing them out," answered Gerald.

" Then, for Heaven's sake, see the fuse isn't too long," he replied. " Just over an inch is enough for traverse work, or they'll bung 'em back." (An inch of the fuse used will burn about a second and a half.)

With that the party was off, led by Gerald. And they crept on till, suddenly, the sergeant gripped his arm and muttered : " They're behind the next traverse." And from behind the earth in front came a guttural exclamation in German.

Gerald, gripping a rifle, was quivering with excitement. He stole forward to where the trench bent back behind the traverse, while the two front men came up each with a bomb in his hand to throw, when lighted, over the top. It was at the precise moment that Gerald gave them the signal to light that he met his first German face to face. For, finding all was silent, the enemy had decided to make a little tour of inspection on his own, and just as the two bombs were lit and propelled over the traverse a stout and perspiring Bavarian bumped his head almost on to Gerald's rifle. For a moment Gerald was as surprised as the crouching German, but only for a moment, for the Bavarian's death-grunt, the crack of the rifle, and the roar of the two bombs were almost simultaneous.

. . . . .

"On 'em, boys!" he shouted, jerking out his empty cartridge, and they scrambled round, over the body, into the next bit of trench. Four Germans lay stiff, and two were struggling to get round the next traverse. One did and one did not. The sergeant got him first. Up to the next traverse, and the same process over again; but "Move, move, for Heaven's sake move!" is the motto if you want to keep 'em on the run. And if a German, wounded, tries to trip you—well, halt, everyone, and send for the doctor and a motor-ambulance for the poor chap—I don't think ! For three traverses they went on, and then a voice came from the other side, " We surrender." Oh ! Gerald, Gerald, would that one who knew the sweeps had been there with you ! After all that's been written, why, oh ! why did you not tell them to come to you instead of going to them ? Surely you have read of their callous swinishness, and your sergeant's life was in your keeping ?

There were three of them when he rounded the traverse, and three shots rang out at the same moment. One hit his sergeant in the head and one hit his sergeant in the heart, and one passed between his own left arm and his body, cutting his coat. It was then he saw red, and so did the men who streamed after him.

" Let's stick 'em, sir," said the men, though the Germans had now thrown down their rifles.

" Nothing of the sort," he snarled. " Which of you said ' We surrender ? ' " and with the veins in his forehead standing out he glared at the Germans.

"I did," answered one of them, smiling. "We really thought you would not be such fools as to be taken in."

"Extraordinary, wasn't it?" laughed Gerald. Yes, the ass period had quite passed. His laugh caused the smiling German to stop smiling.

"As you avoided our bombs entirely owing to an unwarrantable mistake on my part— which cost me the life"—he swallowed once or twice and his hands clenched— "the life of a valued man, I can only remedy this loss on your part to the best of my ability."

"Ah, well," answered the German, "we shall no doubt meet after the war and laugh over the episode. All is fair in love and——" He shrugged his shoulders. "And now we are your prisoners."

"Quite so," drawled Gerald. "All ready for a first-class ticket to Donington Hall. You shall now have it. Bring, my lads, three hair-brush grenades and put in four inches of fuse. That's about eight seconds, my dear friends," and he smiled on the Germans, who were now grovelling on their knees.

"Gott in Himmel!" screamed the one

who had spoken, " you would murder us after we have surrendered ? "

Gerald pointed to the dead sergeant lying huddled in the corner. " You had surrendered before you murdered him," he remarked quietly.

VI

AND now I come to the last day that our friend was privileged to spend in the lotus land of Ypres. When he returns let us hope we shall have moved on—the place is a good deal too lotussy for most of us, if the heavily scented air is any criterion. He had had most of the excitements which those who come over to this entertainment can expect to get, and on this last day he got the *bonne bouche*—the cream of the side shows. His battalion had come to the reserve trenches, as I have said, and from there they had gone to an abode of cellars, where the men could wash and rest, for nothing save a direct hit with a seventeen-inch shell could damage them. It was at three o'clock in the morning that Gerald was violently roused from his slumbers by his captain. " Get to the men

at once ! " he ordered. " Respirators to be
put on. They're making the hell of a gas
attack. It seems to have missed these cellars,
but one never knows. Then go and see
what's happening." Upstairs a confused
babel of sound was going on, and upstairs
Gerald sprinted after he had seen his men.
A strange smell hung about in the summer
air ; the peculiar stench of chlorine, luckily
only mild, made him cough and his eyes
smart and finally shut. The water poured
out of them as eddies of wind made the gas
stronger, and for a time he stood there utterly
helpless. All around him men grunted and
coughed, and lurched about helpless as he
was, deprived of sight for the time. He
heard odd fragments of conversation : " The
front line has broken—gassed out. They're
through in thousands—We're done for—
Let's go." And then clear above the shelling, which had now started furiously, he
heard a voice which he recognised as belonging to one of the Staff officers of his
brigade. " The first man who *does* go I
shoot. Sit down ! Keep your pads on, and
wait for orders."

.   .   .   .   .

Down the road came a few stragglers—men who had broken from the front line and from the reserve trenches. One or two were slightly gassed ; one or two were wounded ; several were neither.

" And what are you doing ? " asked the same officer, planting himself in the middle of the road. " Wounded men in there ! The remainder join that party and wait for orders ! "

" But they're through us," muttered a man, pushing past the officer. " I'm off."

" Did you hear my order ? " said the officer sternly catching his arm. " Get in there—or I'll shoot you."

" Lemme go, curse you," howled the man, shaking off his hand and lurching on—while the others paused in hesitation. There was a sharp crack, and with a grunt the man subsided in the road twitching. The Staff officer, turned round, and with his revolver still in his hand pointed to the party sitting down by Gerald. Without a word the men went there.

" I am going up to see what's happening," he told Gerald. " Get these men below in the cellars and keep them there. It's the shelling will do the damage now—the gas is over."

" Was it a bad attack ? " asked Gerald.

" One of the worst we've had. One part of the line has been pierced, but the men have stuck it well everywhere else. Mercifully we've almost avoided it here." And with that he was gone.

.   .   .   .   .

Two hours later the wounded started to come down the road, and with them men who had really been gassed badly—probably through having mislaid their pads and not being able to find them in time. Some were on stretchers and some were walking. Some ran a few steps and then collapsed, panting and gasping on the road ; some lurched into the ditch and lay there vomiting, and on them all impartially there rained down a hail of shrapnel. In the dressing station they arranged them in rows ; and that day two sweating doctors handled over seven hundred cases. For the gassed men, wheezing, gasping, fighting for breath, with their faces green and their foreheads dripping, they could do next to nothing. In ambulances they got them away as fast as they could down the shell-swept road—and still they came pouring in without cessation. Gerald, watching the poor, struggling crowd, swore softly under his breath. He hadn't seen gas and its effects before, and the first time you see it you generally feel like killing something German to ease the strain. And it was at this moment that a bursting shell scattered a bunch of staggering men and almost blew an officer coming down the road into his arms.

The officer smiled at him feebly and then wiped some froth from his lips with the back of his hand. He stood there swaying, his breath coming and going like a horse that's touched in the wind after being galloped. Out of one sleeve the blood was pouring, and with his hand he'd made a great smear of blood across his mouth. His face was green, and the gas sweat was all over him.

" Good God ! " muttered Gerald. " Sit down, my dear fellow."

" No," he answered ; " I must get on." He spoke slowly and with terrible difficulty, passing his tongue over his lips from time to time and staring fixedly at Gerald. " Where is the general? I have been sent to give him a message." With a dreadful tearing noise in his throat, he started to try to be sick. The paroxysm lasted about five minutes, and then he pulled himself together again.

. . . . .

"Give me the message. I'll take it," said Gerald quietly.

"Listen," said the officer, sitting down and heaving backwards and forwards. "Listen, for I'm done in. They've broken through on our left. There aren't many of them, but our left has had to give." Another paroxysm came on, and the poor lad rolled in the gutter, twisting and squirming. "The gas caught me in my dug-out," he croaked, "and I couldn't find my pad. Just like me, always lose everything." Gerald supported his head, and again wiped the froth from his mouth. "Our men," and the wheezing voice continued at intervals, "our men are gassed to blazes, but they're all up there. They've not fallen back except on the left, where they were up in the air. Poor chaps! Lying in heaps being sick. Noise in trenches like bellows out of work. It's a swine's game, this gas" Again the tearing and gasping.

" Tell the gunners to fire. For God's sake get 'em to fire. Their infantry all over the place, and we're getting about one shell of ours to twenty of theirs. Oh, God, this is awful ! " and he tore at his collar.

" I'll go and find the general at once," said Gerald.

The officer nodded. " Good. I'll stop here till I'm better, and then I suppose I must go back to the boys. Poor devils ! and I'm away out of it." He croaked hideously. " My men never budged, and now they're being shelled to bits—and they're helpless. Get reserves, man ; get reinforcements. For Heaven's sake, hurry. No one seems to know what's happening—and it's been awful up there."

.   .   .   .   .

And so Gerald left him sitting by the side of the road, his eyes staring fixedly at nothing, periodically wiping the froth from his lips with a hand that left a crimson smear wherever it touched. And there the stretcher-bearers found him ten minutes later—one of hundreds of similar cases reported so tersely as " suffering from gas poisoning." And here—having staggered across our horizon—he passes out

again. Whether he lived or died I know not
—that man with the shattered arm and wet
green face, who had brought back the message
from the men whose left flank was sur-
rounded.

All I know is that a quarter of an hour
later Gerald was giving the report to the
general—a report which confirmed the opinion
of the situation which the Staff had already
formed. Half an hour later Gerald's battalion
was ordered to counter-attack and, if they
could get as far, fill the gap. Exactly five
minutes from the time when the battalion
passed the reserve trenches and, in extended
order, pressed forward, my hero took it.
He took it in the leg, and he took it in the
arm from a high-explosive shrapnel, and
went down for the count. They didn't get
back all the ground lost, but they did very
nearly—though of this Gerald knew nothing.
He was bad—distinctly bad. He remembers
dimly the agony the ambulance gave his arm
that night, and has hazy recollections of a
dear woman in a hospital train. He had
landed at Havre on a Tuesday ; that day
fortnight he left Boulogne in a hospital ship.
Back up the ancestral home founded on some-

thing in tins he will go in due course ; back to those same beautiful things—creations was the word—who graced the ancestral drawing-room some months ago.

The situation is fraught with peril. As I have whispered, his income will be something over five figures one day, and the creations have taken up nursing.

But, somehow or other, his views on life have changed, and I think the creations may have their work cut out.

THE END OF "WIPERS"

A SKETCH WRITTEN DURING THE FIRST
WEEK OF MAY

A NICE balmy day, a good motor-car, and a first-class lunch in prospect. Such was my comparatively enviable state less than a month ago. True, the motor-car's springs had had six months' joy riding on the roads of Flanders, and the lunch was to be in Ypres; but one can't have everything— and Wipers was quite a pleasant spot then. In the square, souvenir hunters wandered through the Cloth Hall and the cathedral intent on strange remnants of metal for the curious at home. Tobacco shops did a roaring trade—market day was on. Villainous fragments of fried fish changed hands for a consideration, and everyone was happy and contented.

Into a delightful little shop I ultimately found my way. Twelve small tables, spread with spotless linen, and, needless to say, full of officers satisfying the inner man, presided over by two charming French girls, seemed good enough for me, and, sure enough, the luncheon was on a par with the girls, which is saying "some" in the vernacular. As I left with a consignment of the most excellent white wine, for thirsty officers elsewhere, two soldiers passed me.

"Say, Bill," said one, "this 'ere Wipers is a bit of orl right. They can leave me here as long as they likes." And as I crossed the railway at the western end of the town, one shell passed sullenly overhead, the first I had heard that day—the only discordant note, the only sound of war. That was a month ago.

.   .   .   .   .

A fortnight ago duty took me past the same little shop and through the square. This time I did not linger—there were no souvenir hunters; there was no market-day. Again I was in a motor-car, but this time I rushed through—hoping for the best. Instead of one shell they came in their hundreds. A drunken, swaying noise through the air, like a tramway-car going homewards on its last journey down an empty road, a crash and the roar of the explosion, mixed

with the rumble of falling masonry.   Another
house gone in the dead city.   Huge holes
clawed up in the *pavé* road, and in every corner
dead and twisted horses.   Children lying
torn in the gutter, women and men gaping
in their death agony.   Here and there a
soldier ; legs, arms, fragments of what were
once living, breathing creatures.   And in
nearly every house, had one gone in, little
groups of civilians still moaning and muttering feebly.   They had crept into their homes,
frightened, terrified—to wait for the death
that must come.   And without cessation
came the shells.   In one corner a motor-
ambulance stood drunkenly on three wheels ;
in the middle a wagon overturned with four
dead horses still fast in the traces, and underneath them stuck out two legs, the legs of
what had been the lead driver.   A city of
the dead—not a sign of visible life, save
only our car picking its way carefully through
dead horses and masses of bricks fallen across
the road.   Yesterday's tobacco buyers stiff
in the gutters ; yesterday's vendors of fish
dying in some corner like rats in a trap ;
yesterday's luncheon-shop a huge hole in
the wall with the rafters twisted and broken,

and the floor of the room above scattered over the twelve tables with the spotless linen. And perhaps—worst of all—the terrible, all-pervading stench which seemed to brood like a pall over everything.

At last we were clear of the square and getting into the open east of the town. Over the bridge and up a slight incline—then clear above the noise of the car for one most unpleasant second we heard the last tram going home. The next second a deafening roar, and we were in the centre of the stifling black fumes of a present from Krupps. All would have been well but for a dead horse in the centre of the road, which caused an abrupt stop. We left the car till the fumes had cleared away, and stumbled, gasping into the air, with the water pouring out of our eyes and the fumes catching our throats. And it was then we saw yesterday's Tommy who had regarded " Wipers" as a " bit of orl right."

Staggering down the road came three men, lurching from side to side, bumping up against one another, then falling apart : ever and anon collapsing in the road or the gutter, disappearing into shell holes, tripping

over débris, over trees, over dead things.
Gasping and panting they came on with their
legs not strong enough to hold them.   Nearer
they came, and their faces were yellow-green,
and their foreheads were thick with sweat,
though the evening was chilly.   They were
half-sobbing, half-moaning, with their collars
open and their clothes coated in mud.   And
one of them had a great gash over his head.
Just before they reached us he collapsed
in the ditch — for the last time.   He was
leaning forward and heaving with the agony
of getting his breath.   A froth was forming
on his mouth, and his face was green.

" In God's name what is it ? " we asked
one of the other two as they staggered by.
He stared at us vacantly, gasped out the one
word, " Gas," and disappeared into the
shambles of Ypres.   We had not seen it
before.   We have since, and the first horror
of it is past : but as there is a heaven above,
there is not a man who has seen its effects
who would not give every worldly possession
he has to be able slowly to dribble the con-
tents of a cylinder of the foulest and most
diabolical invention yet conceived into a
trench full of the originators of a device which

most savages would be ashamed to use. We
picked up the poor devil in the ditch and
got him to a dressing station. He died in
fearful agony half an hour after, so I subsequently heard. That was a fortnight ago.

. . . . .

Four nights ago there was a great light in
the sky. Standing up out of the blaze what
was left of the cathedral showed up like a
blackened sentinel. Through the trees the
yellow flames shone with a lurid glow, and
the crashing of falling houses completed the
destruction started by German shells. The
sight was one which will never be forgotten
by those who saw it—that final gutting of
a stricken town. For three days and three
nights it blazed, and now all is over. It is
the best end for that historic city—the
scene of so much senseless carnage. How
many of its harmless inhabitants have perished
with it will never be known—will probably
never be even guessed at. But fire is a puri-
fier, and purification was necessary in Ypres.

THE BLACK SHEEP

FRIZENBURG, APRIL 30, 1915

No one could have called Herbert Jones
brilliant : his best friend—if he possessed
such a thing—would not have predicted a
great future for him. Into the manner of
his living during the first twenty years of his
life it would be well not to enquire too closely.
Herbert Jones—more generally known to
his intimates as 'Erb—was a dweller in dark
places ; one of the human flotsam who
emerge like rats from their holes at night
and spend in the nearest gin palace the few
pence they have nefariously earned during
the day. He was just a product of the gutter ;
from the gutter he came and to the gutter
he returned in the fullness of time. And this
was the way of it.

Personally I never made the acquaintance
of Herbert Jones : such information as I
possess of his disreputable history was told
me one night at a dreary cross-roads three or

four miles east of Ypres, with the greenish flares lighting the sky all around us and the stench of dead horses in our nostrils. My informant was one of my drivers who had lived in the same street with him in London.

What it was that had caused a temporary ebullition of decent feeling in such an unpromising subject I was unable to find out. It was something to do with a lady called Lizzie Green, too much gin, and a picture palace which displayed a film of the Royal Horse Artillery galloping into action. In view of the fact that ninety per cent. of Herbert's income was derived from making himself a public pest at jobbing stables, he quite naturally posed as a horsey youth, and that fact, coupled with Lizzie, the gin, and the film, apparently produced this one ebullition of decent feeling of which I have spoken. He enlisted. The very next day he presented his unprepossessing personality at a recruiting office—and his slum knew him no more. The Royal Regiment swallowed him up, gave him a uniform, decent food, and prepared to make a man of him.

It failed—hopelessly, dismally. The revilings of officers, the cursings of sergeants,

the blasphemy of bombardiers alike failed
to produce the slightest effect. His conduct
sheet rapidly assumed the appearance of a
full-sized novel ; but there he was and there
he remained—a driver in the Field Artillery,
and the black sheep of his battery.

. . . . .

A year later found him at Havre. From
there he drifted to Rouen—reviled by everyone who had the misfortune to have anything
to do with him. At last, like a bad penny,
he turned up again at his old battery, to the
horror of all concerned, who thought they
had effectually got rid of him at the beginning of the war. But the ways of record
officers are wonderful—passing the ways of
women. So when the news was broken to
the major, and he had recovered, he ordered
him to be put with the ammunition limbers,
whose job it is to take ammunition to the
battery nightly when they are in action and
then return [for more. And the captain,
whose job is largely ammunition supply, heard
his history from the sergeant whose job is
entirely ammunition supply, and their remarks would be unprintable. Two nights
later the battery was in action in the salient

5

somewhere east of Ypres, and the reserves of
ammunition were away back somewhere to
the west, and Herbert Jones was with the
reserves.

In the official *communiqués* it was known
as a time of artillery activity in the neighbourhood of Ypres : in the *communiqués* of the
battery it was known as a time of hell let
loose ; but especially was it so known among
the ammunition limbers who nightly passed
from west to east with full limbers and returned from east to west with empty ones.
For, as may be seen by anyone who takes
the trouble to procure an ordnance map,
all roads from the west converge on Ypres,
and having passed through the neck of the
bottle diverge again to the east ; which fact
is not unknown to the Germans. So the
limbers do not linger on the journey, but,
at an interval of ten yards or so, they travel
as fast as straining horseflesh and sweating
drivers can make them. In many places
a map is not necessary—even to a stranger.
The road is clearly marked by what has been
left at its side—the toll of previous journeys
of limbers, who went out six in number and
returned only four. And, should the stranger

be blind, another of his senses will lead him unfailingly along the right road, for these derelict limbers and their horses have been there some time.

· · · · ·

The Germans were searching the road leading to Ypres from the cross-roads where I sat waiting for an infantry working party that had gone astray, on the first of the two occasions on which I saw 'Erb: that is to say, they were plastering a bit of the road with shells in the hope of bagging anything living on that bit. In the distance the rumble of wagons up the road was becoming louder every minute. All around us—for it was a salient—green flares lit up the sky, showing where the front trenches lay, and occasional rolls of musketry, swelling to a crescendo and then dying fitfully away, came at intervals from different parts of the line. A few spent bullets pinged viciously overhead, and almost without cessation came the angry roar of high-explosive shrapnel bursting along the road or over the desolate plough on each side. Close to me, at the cross-roads itself, stood the remnants of a village—perhaps ten houses in all. The flares shone through the ruined

walls—the place stank of death. Save for
the noise it was a Dead World — a no
man's land. In the little village two motor-
ambulances balanced themselves like drunken
derelicts. Dead horses lay stiff and distended
across the road, and a few overturned
wagons completed the scene of desolation.

Then, suddenly, over a slight rise swung
the ammunition limbers—grunting, cursing,
bumping into shell holes and out again. I
watched them pass and swing away right-
handed. In the rear came six pairs of horses,
spare—in case. And as the last one went by
a man beside me said, "Hullo! there's Erb."
It was then I got his history.

An hour later I was back at that same
place, having caught my wandering infantry party and placed them on a line with
instructions to dig and continue digging
till their arms dropped off. But when I got
there I found it had changed a little in
appearance, that dreary cross-roads. Just
opposite the bank where I had sat were two
horses lying in the road and the legs of a
man stuck out from underneath them, and
they had not been there an hour before. The
horses' heads were turned towards Ypres,

and it seemed to me that there was something familiar in the markings of one of them.

With the help of my drivers we pulled out the man. It was no good—but one never knows.

And the same voice said, " Why, it's 'Erb."

Crashing back on the return journey, the limbers empty, 'Erb again bringing up the rear with the spares, one blinding flash, and——

We laid him in the gutter.

Did I not say that he came from the gutter ? And to the gutter he returned in the fullness of time.

JAMES AND THE LAND MINE

A COMPARATIVELY TRUTHFUL ACCOUNT OF AN UNPLEASING EPISODE

THE reasons in triplicate which I gave to the general as to why the land mines had exploded at the wrong time are neither here nor there. Officially he accepted them, but it was all very trying, and entirely due to James.

James is a great thorn in my side; he always has been. He is always doing unexpected things—thereby causing much alarm and despondency among everyone who has the doubtful pleasure of his acquaintance. The last time I saw him before the war was at the Pytchley Hunt ball some eighteen months ago, and though I hesitate to give the incident which occurred there in view of possible doubts being cast on my veracity, and also because of its apparently trifling nature, yet its connection with the sad failure of the land mines is too deep for me to disregard it.

Know then that James had on a pair of

trenches a somewhat hazardous one. Should one of these flares fall on the ground, so that you are between it and the Germans, the only way to escape detection is to lie perfectly motionless until it burns out. All of which tends to make progress slow. It was while one of them was burning itself out, and I was endeavouring to set a safe course between two shell holes and a dead German, that James appeared out of the blue from nowhere. He had six German helmets, a few bayonets, and a variety of other trophies, and was making a noise like a wagonful of saucepans on a cobbled road.

" Dear old boy," he cried, dropping everything on the ground, " it's the deuce of a time since I've seen you."

" It is one of the few things for which I can honestly return thanks," I remarked somewhat shortly. " Would you like a megaphone to tell them I'm coming up to work on that trench in front ? "

" What are you going to do ? " he demanded.

" Fill it in and mine it when I can find it."

" Splendid," he answered. " I'm your man. These," and he kicked the trophies,

which promptly gave forth a crashing noise,
" all come from it. I've just been there. I
will guide you."

Under normal circumstances I would as
soon have been guided by a young elephant ;
but, as I say, James is difficult—very difficult.

" I think there are one or two Germans in
it," he whispered as we crawled on. " I
heard one talking and threw a bomb over the
traverse, but as I'd forgotten to light it it
didn't go off."

The next instant he disappeared and the
procession came to an abrupt halt. A wallow-
ing noise was heard, and James's head came
into view again. " This is the trench," he
remarked tersely, " the cess-pit end." It
was one of the few occasions that night that
I laughed.

My subaltern extended the men while I
entreated James to go. I thanked him for
his valuable assistance and earnestly begged
him to depart. He could help me no more,
and I knew there would be a calamity if he
remained. It was all in vain, James was out
for a night of it, so ultimately I left him to
his own devices and departed to see what
was happening. I found everything quite

peaceful; six land mines were lying at the bottom of a bit of trench where we could get them when wanted, and the trench, all except about thirty yards, was being filled in. The thirty yards would be filled in later and would be mined. One could hear the Germans talking in their trenches, and for the moment an air of complete calm brooded over the scene.

. . . . .

No sniper sniped, no gunner gunned. A few gaunt trees creaked slightly in the breeze, and an occasional rifle crack came sharply through the night from farther down the line. Then James fell into the trench again. This time he missed the cess-pit and hit a German. As I have said before, it was all most annoying.

A worrying noise was heard, and every one fell flat on his face as a rapid fusillade broke out from all directions. Flares went up by the score and everything became unpleasantly lively. The only person who seemed quite oblivious of all the turmoil was James. He suddenly loomed up in front of me dragging a diminutive Boche behind him.

" Do you remember "—his voice was quite

shaken with rage—" the accursed swine-dog of a waiter at the Pytchley Hunt ball who laughed when I sat on the grapes ? I have him here."

" Lie still, you fool," I muttered. " Do you want to get every one ' scuppered ' ? "

Of course, James paid not the slightest attention. " I have him here," he grunted. " I know that scar, you horrible reptile," and he shook the little brute till his teeth rattled. " Are you aware that you spoilt the best pair of silk breeches I ever had, and I haven't paid for them yet ? " And with that he threw him into the trench close by.

Like James at the ball, he sat down and arose hurriedly. James would select the bit of trench where the land mines were. There was a most deafening roar as all six went off, and that waiter will undoubtedly wait no more. James himself, I'm glad to say, was stunned, which kept him quiet for a time, but he was about the only quiet thing in France for the next hour. It is my personal belief that in addition to all the batteries on each side which opened fire simultaneously, the mysterious gun which has bombarded Dunkirk let drive as well.

For two hours I lay in a wet trench, with a pick in the small of my back and James on top of me. About three we all went home, rather the worse for wear. James said he had a headache and wouldn't play any more. I got one giving my reasons to the general in triplicate.

THE SIXTH DRUNK

TO A VERY GALLANT IRISHMAN, WHO DIED IN
NOVEMBER, 1914

" No. 10,379 Private Michael O'Flannigan, you are charged, first, with being absent from roll-call on the 21st instant until 3.30 a.m. on the 22nd, a period of five hours and thirty minutes ; second, being drunk ; third, assaulting an N.C.O. in the execution of his duty."

The colonel leant back in his chair in the orderly-room and gazed through his eyeglass at the huge bullet-headed Irishman standing on the other side of the table.

The evidence was uninteresting, as such evidence usually is, the only humorous relief being afforded by the sergeant of the guard on the night of the 21st, who came in with an eye of cerulean hue which all the efforts of his painstaking wife with raw beefsteak had been unable to subdue. It appeared from his evidence that he and Private O'Flannigan had had a slight difference of opinion, and

that the accused had struck him in the face
with his fist.

"What have you got to say, Private O'Flannigan?"

"Shure, 'twas one of the boys from Water-
ford, sorr, I met in the town yonder, and we
put away a bit of the shtuff. I would not
be denying I was late, but I was not drunk
at all. And as for the sergeant, sure 'twas
messing me about he was and plaguing me,
and I did but push him in the face. Would
I be hitting him, and he a little one?"

The colonel glanced at the conduct-sheet
in his hand; then he looked up at O'Flannigan.

"Private O'Flannigan, this is your fifth
drunk. In addition to that you have struck
a non-commissioned officer in the execution
of his duty, one of the most serious crimes
a soldier can commit. I'm sick of you.
You do nothing but give trouble. The next
drunk you have I shall endeavour to get you
discharged as incorrigible and worthless. As
it is, I shall send you up for court-martial.
Perhaps they will save me the trouble. March
out."

"Prisoner and escort—right turn—quick
6

march ! " The sergeant-major piloted them through the door ; the incident closed.

.   .   .   .   .

Now all that happened eighteen months ago. The rest is concerning the sixth drunk of Michael O'Flannigan and what he did ; and it will also explain why at the present moment, in a certain depot mess in England, there lies in the centre of the dinner-table, every guest night, a strange jagged-looking piece of brown earthenware. It was brought home one day in December by an officer on leave, and it was handed over by him to the officer commanding the depot. And once a week officers belonging to the 13th and 14th and other battalions gaze upon the strange relic and drink a toast to the Sixth Drunk.

It seems that during November last the battalion was in the trenches round Ypres. Now, as all the world knows, at that time the trenches were scratchy, the weather was vile, and the Germans delivered infantry attacks without cessation. In fact, it was a most unpleasing and unsavoury period. In one of these scratchy trenches reposed the large bulk of Michael O'Flannigan. He

did not like it at all—the permanent defensive
which he and everyone else were forced into.
It did not suit his character. Along with
O'Flannigan there were a sergeant and three
other men, and at certain periods of the day
and night the huge Irishman would treat the
world to an impromptu concert. He had a
great deep bass voice, and when the mood
was on him he would bellow out strange
seditious songs—songs of the wilds of Ireland
—and mingle with them taunts and jeers at
the Germans opposite.

Now these bursts of song were erratic, but
there was one period which never varied.
The arrival of the rum issue was invariably
heralded by the most seditious song in
O'Flannigan's very seditious repertory.

One evening it came about that the Huns
tactlessly decided to deliver an attack just
about the same time as the rum was usually
issued. For some time O'Flannigan had been
thirstily eyeing the traverse in his trench
round which it would come—when suddenly
the burst of firing all along the line proclaimed
an attack. Moreover, it was an attack in
earnest. The Huns reached the trenches and
got into them, and, though they were twice

driven out, bit by bit the battalion retired. O'Flannigan's trench being at the end and more or less unconnected with the others, the Germans passed it by : though, as the sergeant in charge very rightly realised, it could only be a question of a very few minutes before it would be untenable.

" Get out," he ordered, " and join up with the regiment in the trenches behind."

" And phwat of the issue of rum ? " demanded Michael O'Flannigan, whose rifle was too hot to hold.

" You may think yourself lucky,my bucko, if you ever get another," said the sergeant. " Get out."

.   .   .   .   .

O'Flannigan looked at him. " If you're after thinking that I would be leaving the rum to them swine you are mistaken, sergeant."

" Are you going, O'Flannigan ? "

"Bedad, I'm not !   Not if the King himself was asking me."

At that moment a Boche rounded the traverse. With a howl of joy O'Flannigan hit him with the butt of his rifle. From that moment he went mad.   He hurled himself over the traverse and started. It was full of Germans—but this wild apparition finished them. Roaring like a bull and twisting his rifle round his head like a cane, the Irishman fell on them—and as they broke, he saw in the corner the well-beloved earthenware pot containing the rum. He seized the thing in his right hand and poured most of the liquid down his throat, while the rest of it ran over his face and clothes. And then Michael O'Flannigan ran amok. His great voice rose high above the roar of the rifles, as, with the empty rum jar in one hand and his clubbed rifle in the other he went down the trench.

What he must have looked like with the red liquid pouring down his face, his hands covered with it, his clothes dripping with it, in that eerie half-light, Heaven knows. He was shouting an old song of the Fenian days, and it is possible they thought he was the devil. He was no bad substitute anyway. And then of a sudden his regiment ceased to shoot from the trenches behind and a voice cried, "O'Flannigan." It passed down the line, and, as one man, they came back howling, "O'Flannigan." They drove the

Germans out like chaff and fell back into the lost trenches—all save one little party, who paused at the sight in front of them. There stood O'Flannigan astride the colonel, who was mortally wounded. They heard rather than saw the blow that fetched home on the head of a Prussian officer—almost simultaneously with the crack of his revolver. They saw him go down with a crushed skull, while the big earthenware jar shivered to pieces. They saw O'Flannigan stagger a little and then look round—still with the top of the rum jar in his hand.

" You are back," he cried.   " It is well, but the rum is gone."

And then the colonel spoke. He was near death and wandering. " The regiment has never yet lost a trench. Has it, O'Flannigan, you scoundrel ? "   And he peered at him.

" It has not, sorr," answered the Irishman.

" I thought," muttered the dying officer, " there were Prussians in here a moment ago."

" They were, sorr, but they were not liking it, so they went."

Suddenly the colonel raised himself on his elbow. " What's the matter with you,

O'Flannigan ?   What's that red on your
face ?   It's rum, you blackguard.   You're
drunk again."   His voice was growing weaker.
" Sixth time . . . discharged . . . incorrigible and worthless."   And with that he died.

They looked at O'Flannigan, and he was
sagging at the knees.   " Bedad! 'tis not all
rum, the red on me, colonel, dear."

He slowly collapsed and lay still.

And that is the story of the strange table
adornment of the depot mess, the depot of
the regiment who have never yet lost a
trench.

THE MINE

SOME ARE BORN HUNS, AND OTHERS HAVE
HUNS THRUST UPON THEM

"LAST night we exploded a mine under a redoubt in the enemy's trenches, and successfully occupied the crater. A considerable number of Germans were killed." Thus the official communiqué.

And yet the great powers that be have no idea that this small local success was entirely due to David Jones—sometime miner in a coal-field in South Wales. In fact, the betting is about a fiver to an acid drop that they have no idea that he exists. Bar the police in his local village, who disliked him intensely, and his N.C.O.'s out here, who disliked him still more, very few people do know that he exists. Undersized, in every way an undesirable acquaintance, a silent and morose man, it is nevertheless an undoubted fact that had it not been for David Jones, the aforementioned crater would not have been occupied, and the considerable number of defunct Germans would now be alive. And this was the way of it.

The presence of David in such an unhealthy locality as Flanders was entirely due to his regrettable lack of distinction between *meum* and *tuum*. Exactly what occurred is immaterial, but deciding that the evils he knew of in the shape of prison were probably worse than the evils he did not know of, in the shape of the Hun, our friend managed to evade the too pressing attentions of the police, and in due course found himself across the water in one of the new formed Tunnelling Companies. These companies are composed almost entirely of those who from their earliest infancy have been reared in the atmosphere of moles rather than in the atmosphere of men, and have as their work out here the great game of mining and countermining. Early in the proceedings it became apparent to those whose duty and privilege it was to command David Jones that his affection for woolly bears, pip squeaks, crumps, Marias, and others of the great *genus obus* was not of that type which passeth the love of women.

It is even rumoured that on one occasion, in a wood behind the line which was receiving attention from the Hun, and in which lay our hero's temporary abode, he made a voluntary confession of several real and a few imaginary misdeeds of his early youth in the hope of being sent back to prison and safety. Which is all by the way.

In the course of time, however, the Tunnelling Company was called upon to justify its existence—to become again as moles and not men, to gasp and sweat in the bowels of the earth—and thus the wood where they had been knew them no more. In front of our line, poked out a little from the German lines, there lay a semi-circular redoubt. It was strong, very strong, as many officers in many regiments of foot will confirm. The ground in front of it bore eloquent testimony to frequent unsuccessful attempts to dislodge the enemy. Gunners had gunned it preparatory to assaults, gunners had gunned it all day and every day for many days, but so far in vain. Always were the infantry met with the same deadly cross machine-gun fire did they set foot over our parapet. Wherefore having failed to subdue it from the air, and over the ground, they sent for the miners and told them to try from underneath. And thus it was that David Jones came again to his natural element.

Now I venture to think that of that natural element comparatively little is known by those who remain in the island over the water. The charge of cavalry, the thunder of guns, the grim infantry attack through the swirling mists of dawn, these can be visualised, can be imagined. Pictures by artists, quite a small percentage of which are more or less accurate, give to those who have never seen the dread drama of war a tolerably accurate impression of what happens. But of David Jones's natural element, of that work which goes on day and night, ceaselessly, burrowing under the ground nearer, ever nearer, the goal, there are no pictures to draw. And so before I come to tell of what my ruffian miner did under the earth in the place where the infantry had charged so often in vain, and of the German engineer officer who was discovered with part of his helmet forced into his brain and his head split asunder, I would digress for a space, and try to the best of my ability to paint

that setting in which the human moles live
and move and have their being.

.　　.　　.　　.　　.

I would take those who may care to follow
me to the front-line trenches, where at a
certain place—a sap head, perchance, or a
Johnson hole just behind, or even in the
trench itself—a deep, shored up shaft has been
sunk. From the front nothing is visible, and,
by suitable screening, the inquisitive ones
who fly overhead are prevented from seeing
anything to cheer them up and make them
excited. At the bottom of the shaft two
men are sitting shovelling a heap of loose
earth into buckets. Each bucket as it is
filled is hoisted up on a rope working on a
pulley—only to be lowered again empty
when the earth has been tipped into some
convenient shell hole, screened from the sight
of the gentlemen opposite. If seen, the
steady exodus of earth from a trench at one
point is apt to give the Hun furiously to
think—always an unwise proceeding. In
front of the two men is a low black hole from
which at regular intervals there comes a
man, stripped to the waist, glistening with
sweat, pushing a small trolley on leathered

wheels. While the two men silently tip up
the trolley and empty out the earth, he
stands blinking for a moment at the patch
of blue sky, only to disappear into the low,
black hole, his trolley empty. Everything
is silent; there is no hurry. Perhaps the
occasional zip of a bullet, a lazy crump of a
shell down the line; that is all, that and the
low, black hole—ominous, sinister, the entrance to the mine.

And now mind your head; let us follow
the man with the empty trolley. From far
ahead comes the muffled thud of a pick, and
behind one the light of day is streaming
through the opening of the gallery. Bent
almost double, one creeps forward, guiding
oneself by one's hands as they touch walls
that feel dank and cold. Then a turning, and
utter, absolute darkness, until far ahead a
faint light appears, the light at the front face
of the mine. Another man pushing a full
trolley squeezes past you, his body gleaming faintly white in the darkness, while
steadily, without cessation, by the light of an
electric lamp, the man on the front face goes
on picking, picking, his body glistening as
if it had been dipped in oil. When he is

tired, another takes his place ; there is no
pause. Each yard as it is taken out is
shored up with mine cases and sheeting, otherwise the whole thing may collapse on your
head.

As you go on, your hands against the sides,
you will find possibly an opening on one side
or the other—the opening of another gallery,
a gallery with a T head at the end, all finished.
No earth is being carted from here, there is
for the time no one in it ; it is a listening
gallery, and with the listening gallery and
all it stands for we come to grips with the
real drama of mining. Were it merely the
mechanical removal of earth, the mechanical
making of a tunnel from one place to another,
it would perhaps be a safer occupation, but
just as inspiring to write about as a new
cure for corns. Moreover, it was from a
listening gallery that David Jones—still, all
in good time.

Mining, like most games, is one at which
two can play, and it is not a matter of great
surprise that neither side will allow the other
one to play unmolested. Therefore, where
there is mining there also is countermining,
and the two operations are not exactly the

same. For while mining is essentially an offensive act designed to blow up a portion of the enemy's trenches and form a crater in which men may shelter, countermining is essentially a defensive act designed merely to wreck the advancing mine. Thus both sides may at the same time be running out a mine towards the opposite trenches, and also a countermine in another part of the line to meet the hostile mine. Moreover, in a mine the charge is large, to effect as much damage as possible ; in a countermine the charge is small, in order not to make too large a crater in which the enemy may unscrupulously take up his abode. All of which is essential for the proper understanding of David Jones —his act.

At periods, therefore, during the twenty-four hours all work in the mine is suspended. The muffled tapping of the pick ceases, and silence as of the grave reigns in the underground world. And during this period in each of the listening galleries skilled men stand with their ears glued to the earth, and some with instruments of which I may not speak, and listen. There under the earth, with their dead lying above them, in that

No Man's Land between the trenches, with ears strained in the silence, a silence that can be felt, they listen for that dread noise, the muffled tap-tap of the enemy's miners countermining towards them. Sometimes the mine goes through without any countermine at all —more often not. Frequently the countermine is exploded too soon, or the direction is wrong and no damage is done, but sometimes it is otherwise. Sometimes there will be a dull, rumbling explosion—a few mine cases will fly upwards from the centre of the ground between the trenches, perhaps a boot or a head, but nothing more. And the miners will mine no more. The countermine has been successful.

But the estimation of distance and direction under the ground by listening to the muffled tap of the other man is a tricky business, and depends on many things. A fissure in the right direction, and it will sound close to, when in reality it is far away ; an impervious strata across your front, and it will sound afar off, when in reality it is near.

Which all goes to show that it is a game of chance. But I would ask the arm-chair

critic, the man in the street, if he have a
spark of imagination, to transport himself to
a mine where there is yet ten yards to go.
Whenever for a space the moles stop, and
the underworld silence settles like a pall,
they hear the tap-tap of the other workers'
ghostly fingers coming out to meet them.
And then the tap-tap ceases. Have the
others gone in the wrong direction, bearing
away from them, or are they close to, three
or four feet away even now charging the head
of their countermine with explosive ? Shall
they go on, for time is precious, and finish
that ten yards, or shall they stop awhile and
see if they fire their countermine ? Is it safe
to do another two yards before they stop, or
is it even now too late ? Is that great tearing explosion coming at once, in the next
second, or isn't it coming at all ? And all the
time those glistening, sweating men carry on
—pick, pick, pick. It is for the officer in
charge to decide, and until then——

.   .   .   .   .

Now, I don't for a moment think that David
Jones regarded the matter at all in that light.
An overmastering relief at being in a place
where whizz-bangs cease from troubling and

7

pip-squeaks are at rest drove out all lesser thoughts. When it happened he was as nearly contented as he was capable of being. The mine was ready to fire. Its head was well under the centre of the German redoubt, and all the morning slabs of gun-cotton had been carried up to the head. With loving care the electric leads had been taken up, the detonator fixed up—everything was ready. The earth to damp the charge, so laboriously carted out, had been brought back again, to prevent the force of the explosion blowing down the gallery instead of going upwards. And to the casual observer it seemed that the gallery ended merely in a solid wall of earth, into which vanished two harmless-looking black leads.

Now, the mine was going to be fired at seven o'clock in the evening. One does not prepare with great trouble an elaborate affair of that sort and then loose it off at any old time. All the infantry were warned—the gunners were warned—staff officers at discreet distances buzzed like bluebottles. As soon as it went off the infantry were to rush the redoubt, the gunners were to shell behind to prevent the counter-attack, and the staff

were to have dinner. Which was all very
right and proper.

The only one of these details which interested David was the hour at which the mine
was to go off. Until that time he had fully
made up his mind that the T head listening
gallery, where he was comfortably smoking
on a pile of sandbags, was a very much more
desirable place than the trench up above,
where, at or about the hour of five-thirty, the
Hun was wont to hate with shells of great
violence coming from a direction which almost
enfiladed the trench. He recalled with distinct aversion the man next him the previous
evening who had stopped a large piece of
shell with his head.

At the same time he had no intention of
remaining in the T head when the mine went
off. Six-thirty struck him as a good and
propitious moment to take his departure to
the dangers of the upper air. David Jones
was not a man to take any risk that could
be avoided, and the mere fact that every
one had been ordered out of the mine had
no bearing on the subject whatever. Like
his personal courage, his sense of discipline
was nil.

And so in the dark silence of the mine gallery, lying at ease on sandbags, with no horrible whistlings overhead, David Jones settled himself to rest and ruminate, and in the fulness of time he slept.

Now the mining operations had gone without a hitch. Apparently the Hun had no idea that his privacy was going to be invaded, and no sounds of countermining had been heard. Once, very faint in the distance, a tapping had been heard about three days after they had started. Since then it had not been repeated, and the officer in charge was not to be blamed for thinking that he had the show to himself. Nevertheless it is an undoubted fact that the thing which woke David Jones was a large piece of earth falling on his face, and a light shining through the face of the listening gallery. The next moment he heard a muttered ejaculation in a language he did not know, and great masses of earth rained down on his face while the light was extinguished. His training as a miner enabled him to see in a moment what had happened. That part of his mind worked instinctively. A German gallery had opened into their listening gallery. Some strata of soil had rendered it almost sound-less, and his sleep during the last two hours had prevented him hearing the approach through the final two feet. All that he grasped in a flash; but what was far more to the point, he realised that in about two seconds he would be face to face with a hor-rible Hun, a prospect which turned him cold with horror. Had he been capable of getting up, had his legs been capable of overcoming his terror, there is but little doubt that he would have fled to the safety of the open air. After all, a problematic shell is better than an encounter with a large and brutal man underground.

But before he could move, a head and shoulders followed by a body came through the opening and fell almost on top of him. A torch was cautiously flashed, and by its light the trembling David saw a large and brutal-looking man peering round. Then the man moved forward. Evidently he had seen that he was in a gallery off the main one, and had failed to see our hero sheltering behind the sandbags. For a long while there was silence. David could hear the German's heavy breathing, as he stood a few feet from him just where the main gallery crossed the entrance to the T head. He realised that he was afraid to flash his torch until he was quite certain there was no one about.

But now David's mind was moving with feverish activity. So far he had escaped detection—but supposing more of these terrible beings came. Supposing this one came back and did not overlook him again. The thought nerved him to action. Cautiously, without a sound he raised himself from behind the pile of sandbags and crept to the spot where the T head left the short gallery that connected it to the main one, and there he stood in the inky darkness with the German a few feet in front of him. His plan was to make a dash for safety when the German started to explore the main gallery.

It seemed an eternity—in reality it was about half a minute—before the light was again flashed cautiously into the darkness. It cast round in a circle and then came to a halt. He heard the sharp intake of the German's breath, and saw the light fixed on the two black leads. Then things moved quickly.

The German laid down his pick, and fumbled in his pocket for his wire-cutters. Those leads told their story plain for all to read. Again, in a flash, the dangers of his position struck David. This accursed Hun would cut the leads and then return, and run straight into him. He wouldn't bother to explore the gallery further. He would merely murder him, and pass on. A horrible thought.

With infinite caution he reached for the pick. The German was muttering to himself and trying to detach his wire-cutters from his belt. At last he had them free, and, flashing his torch once again, stooped forward to cut the lead. And as he did so with a grunt, David Jones struck—struck at the centre of the head outlined in the circle of light. There was a dreadful half-choked cry and—silence.

.   .   .   .   .

Two minutes later David Jones was in the trench looking fearfully over his shoulder as if expecting pursuit. The idea of warning the officer in charge that a German gallery had struck through into theirs never even entered his head It was a matter of complete indifference to him if another Hun came in and cut the wire, so long as he wasn't on hand to be cut too. So it was fortunate perhaps that David had overslept himself, as one minute after his arrival in the upper earth there was a deafening thunderous roar. A great mass of earth, roots, wood, and other fragments flew upwards and then came raining down again. The infantry were across in a flash—the curtain of shrapnel descended—and the staff had dinner.

There were two things that no one ever cleared up satisfactorily. One was the presence of a miner's pick, of a pattern different to that in use in the British Army, in the tool dump of a certain Tunnelling Company. But it was a very small thing, and no one worried.

The other was the presence of a German Engineer Officer in the mine shaft with his helmet, or part of it, in his brain. Various opinions were given by various people; but as they were all wrong, they don't matter. Anyway, the mine had been most successful —and everybody shook hands with everybody.

All, that is, except David Jones, who was

undergoing Field Punishment Number One for stealing the emergency rum ration and getting drunk on it.

Which is really rather humorous when you come to think of it.

DRIVER ROBERT BROWN

TO THE GREAT ARMY OF THOSE WHO HAVE
PASSED DOWN THE LONG VALE, UNSUNG,
UNHONOURED

FOUR or five years ago, in the dim, hazy time
when Europe lay at peace, there arrived at
the station in England where I was fortunate
enough to be serving a batch of eight re-
cruits. They were very raw and very un-
trained, and it was the doubtful pleasure of
the unit in which I was, to undertake periodically the training of such batches in order
to relieve a somewhat overtaxed depôt elsewhere. This batch—like unto other similar
batches—aspired to become drivers in His
Majesty's Corps of Royal Engineers. Occasionally their aspirations were realised—more
often not, for the terms of their service
were two years with the colours and ten with
the reserve, and at the end of two years the
average man may just about be considered

capable of looking after two horses and a set of harness—really looking after them—and not before. Then they go, or most of them, and the service knows them no more However, all that is beside the point.

Wandering dispassionately round the stables one day, I perceived the eight, mounted on blankets, sitting on their horses, while a satirical and somewhat livery rough-riding corporal commented on the defects of their figures, their general appearance, and their doubtful claim to existence at all, in a way that is not uncommon with rough riders. Then for the first time I saw Brown—Driver Robert Brown, to give him his full name.

" I 'ad a harnt once, No. 3. She was sixty-four, and weighed twenty stone. And if she'd 'a been sitting on that there 'orse of yours she'd have looked just like you : only 'er chest grew in front and not be'ind like yours."

No. 3 was Driver Robert Brown. I passed on. The presence of an officer sometimes tends to check the airy persiflage which flows so gracefully from the lips of riding instructors.

A week after I inquired of the Corporal as

to the progress of his charges. " Not bad, sir," he said—" not bad. The best of them easy is that there Brown. He don't look much on a horse—in fact, he looks like a sack o' potatoes—but 'e's a tryer, and we'll turn 'im into something before we've done."

Then one day—about four in the afternoon —I happened to wander through the stables. They were deserted apparently save for the stableman—until, in a corner, I came upon Driver Brown. He was giving his horse sugar, and making much of him—to use the riding-school phrase. We had a talk, and he told me things, when he got over his shyness— about his parents and where he lived, and that he loved animals, and a lot else besides. From then on I kept my eye on Brown, and the more I did so, the more I liked him. He was no beauty—he was not particularly smart—but he was one of the best. His N.C.O.'s swore by him—his two horses had never looked better—his harness was spotless. In addition to that he played back in the football eleven, if not with great skill, at any rate with immense keenness. He had exactly the figure for a zealous full back, and was of the type who kicked with such vim that when he missed the ball—which he generally did—he invariably fell heavily to the ground. Thus Robert Brown—recruit.

. . . . .

When his two years were up, Brown elected to stay on in the Service. The Service consisting in this case of his commanding officer, his N.C.O.'s and myself, it could find no reason why he shouldn't—in fact, and on the contrary, many very excellent reasons why he should. So Brown took on for his seven. Shortly afterwards, owing to a marked propensity of my servant to combine the delights of old Scotch with the reprehensible custom of sleeping off those delights in my best easy chair—one bought on the hire system, not the Government issue, where sleep under any circumstances is completely out of the question— owing, as I say, to this unpleasant propensity, I approached my commanding officer. N.C.O.'s were annoyed —they entreated, they implored, and the issue was in doubt, till a providential attack of influenza laid my C.O. low for the time, and the senior subaltern—myself—reigned in his stead. Then the sergeant-major laughed, and resigned himself to the inevitable. Driver

Robert Brown became my servant, and the desecrator of my padded arm-chair retired—after a short period of durance vile—to seek repose on stable buckets.

During the forthcoming six months I am bound to admit I suffered—dreadfully. You do not make a servant in a day ; but he tried his level best. We had shirt parades, in which I instructed him in the art of studding shirts, with little hints thrown in as to the advisability of wreaking his will on the shirt for dinner before he cleaned my parade boots for the following morning—not after. We delved into the intricacies of washing lists, and he waxed indignant over the prices charged. They seemed to me quite ordinary, but Brown would have none of it. I did not often study them—bills were never one of my hobbies ; but one day it suddenly struck me the month's bill was smaller than usual. That was the awful occasion when changing quickly for cricket. I thought something was wrong with the shirt ; it seemed rather stiffer in front than the average flannel—moreover, it had no buttons. Howls for Brown. Vituperation for lack of buttons.

" But, sir, that's an evening shirt you've

got on. One I washed myself to save the washing bill." Tableau.

Then I prepared lists on pieces of paper as to the exact things I required packed in my suit-case when I departed for week-ends. There was the hunting week-end, and the ball-dance week-end, and the week-end when I stayed 'neath the parental roof, and—er— other week-ends too numerous to mention. I would grunt Dance, or Home, or Brighton at him when he brought me my tea on Friday morning, and then during the morning he would, with the aid of the correct list, pack the necessary. There were occasional lapses. Once I remember—it was lunch-time on Friday, and we were being inspected. The mess was full of brass hats, and my train was 2.45. I had howled Dance at Brown as I passed my room before lunch, and was hoping for the best, when the mess waiter told me my servant wanted me for a moment. I went outside.

"Please, sir, them thin ones of yours is full of holes and the other three are at the wash." His voice like himself was good and big. "Shall I run down and buy a pair and meet you at the station."

All the general said when I returned was,
" Did he mean socks ? "

Then there was a dreadful occasion when
he sent me away one week-end with one of
his dickies in my bag—he had been promoted
to mufti—instead of a dress shirt; and
another even more awful when he sent me
to an austere household—prayers at eight,
etc.—from the owner of which I had hopes,
with my boots wrapped in a paper of orange
hue which had better be nameless. I could
continue indefinitely—the mistakes that lad
made would have built a church ; but withal
I never wish for a better servant—a truer-
hearted friend. And all this happened in the
long dim ages way back before we started—
he and I—with thousands of others for the
land across the water ; where for a space
he remained my servant, until in the fullness
of time he passed down that Long Valley
from which there is no return. Many have
passed down it these last months—many will
pass down it before Finis is written on this
World War ; but none deserve a gentler
crossing over the Great Divide than Robert
Brown, Driver, R.E., and sometime batman.

.   .   .   .   .

Now should there be any who, having read as far as this, hopefully continue in the belief that they are getting near the motto—in the shape of some wonderful deed of heroism and daring—they will, I am afraid, be disappointed. I have no startling pegs on which to hang the tale of his life. Like thousands of others, he never did anything very wonderful—he never did anything at all wonderful. He was just one of the big army of Browns out here of whom no one has ever heard. One of that big army who have done their bit unrewarded, unknown—because it was the thing to do ; a feeling unknown to some of those at home—I allude to the genus Maidenhead Maggot still seen in large quantities—er—resting. And yet for each of those Browns—their death recorded so tersely in the paper—some heart-broken woman has sobbed through the long night, watching the paling dawn with tear-stained eyes, aching for the sound of footsteps for ever still, conjuring up again the last time she saw her man, now lying in a nameless grave. Would the Maggot get as much ? I wonder.

As I have said, I'm afraid I haven't got anything very wonderful to describe. You

8

can't make a deathless epic out of a man
being sick—dreadfully sick beside the road
—and an hour afterwards getting your food
for you. It doesn't sound very romantic, I
admit, and yet—— It was in the morning, I
remember, about three o'clock, that we first
smelt it, and we were lying about half a mile
behind the line. That first sweet smell of
chlorine turning gradually into the gasping,
throat-racking fumes. Respirators weren't
regarded with the same importance then as
they are now, but we all had them. Of
course I'd lost mine. Since early childhood
I have invariably lost everything. Brown
found it, and I put it on—and then he disappeared. Some two hours later, when the
shelling had abated a little, and the gas had
long since passed, I found him again. He
was white and sweating, and the gas was in
him—not badly, you understand, not badly—
but the gas was in him. For three or four
hours he was sick, very sick—and his head
was bursting. I know what he felt like.

And I said to the major, " I'm sorry it's
Brown, but it'll teach him a lesson not to
lose his respirator again," for, that is the way
with Thomas Atkins—he is apt to lose most

things that are not attached to him by chains.

It doesn't sound at all romantic all this, does it ?—and yet, well, I found *my* respirator in the pocket of another coat. And as Brown came in with some food—he'd recovered about an hour—I handed him back *his* respirator, and I asked him why he'd done it.

" Well, I thought as 'ow you might 'ave to be giving orders like, and would want it more than me." He spoke quite naturally.

I didn't thank him—I couldn't have spoken to save my life—but the lad knew what I thought. There are some things for which thanks are an insult.

.   .   .   .   .

There was another thing which comes to me too, as I write—nothing very wonderful again, and yet—— In the course of our wanderings we were engaged upon a job of work that caused us to make nightly a pilgrimage through Wipers. At the time Wipers was not healthy. That stage of the war of attrition—I understand that many of the great thinkers call it a war of attrition, though personally I wish they could be here when the Hun is attriting, or whatever the verb is —that stage, then, known as the second battle of Ypres was in progress. And, though all of that modern Pompeii was unhealthy at the time, there were certain marked places particularly so. One such was the Devil's Corner. There, nightly, a large number of things—men and horses—were killed ; and the road was littered with—well, fragments.

Now it chanced one night that I had taken Brown with me to a point inside the salient, and at midnight I had sent him away—back to the field the other side of Ypres, where for the time we were lying. Two or three hours after I followed him, and my way led me past the Devil's Corner. All was quite quiet—the night's hate there was over, at any rate for the moment. One house was burning fiercely just at the corner, and the only sounds that broke the silence were the crackling of the flames and the occasional clatter of a lim- bered wagon travelling fast down a neigh- bouring road. And then suddenly I heard another sound—clear above my own foot- steps. It was the voice of a man singing— at least, when I say singing—it was a noise

of sorts. Also there was no mistaking the
owner of the voice. Too often had I heard
that same voice apostrophising " a beautiful picture, in a beautiful golden fraime."   I
stopped surprised—for what in the name of
fortune Brown was doing in such an unsavoury spot was beyond me! In fact, I felt
distinctly angry. The practice of remaining
in needlessly dangerous places is not one to
be encouraged. I traced that noise ; it came
from behind an overturned limber, with two
defunct horses lying in the ditch. I crossed
the road and peered over.

Sitting in the ditch was Robert Brown, and
on his knees rested the head of the limber
driver. In the breaking dawn you could see
that the end was very near—the driver had
driven for the last time. From the limp sag
of his back I thought it was broken, and a bit
of shell had removed—well, no matter, but one
could hear the beating of the wings. Brown
didn't see me, but occasionally, gentle as a
woman, he bent over him and wiped the
death sweat from his forehead ; while all
the time, under his breath, mechanically, he
hummed his dirge. Then the man, lying half
under the limber, stirred feebly.

" What is it, mate ? " said Brown, leaning forward.

" Take the letters out of my pocket, matey," he muttered. " Them blokes at the War Office takes so long—and send 'em to—to——" The lips framed the words feebly, but no sound came.

" Who to, pal ? " whispered Brown ; but even as he spoke the poor maimed form quivered and lay still. And as I watched Brown lay his head gently down, and close his eyes, the road, the houses seemed to grow a trifle misty. When I next looked up I saw him stumping away down the road, and, as he rounded the corner, a dreadful noise stating that, with regard to a lady named Thora, " he had loved 'er in life too little, 'e 'ad loved 'er in death too well," came floating back in the still air.

Yet methinks no great man's soul, speeded on its way by organ and anthem, ever had a nobler farewell than that limber driver, if the spirit of the singer has anything to do with it.

.   .   .   .   .

But, as I said before, I could continue indefinitely. Was there not the terrible occasion when I found him standing guard over a perfectly harmless Belgian interpreter, with a pick in his hand and the light of battle in his eye, under the impression that he had caught a German spy? The wretched man had lain on the ground for three hours—every movement being greeted with a growl of warning from Brown and a playful flourish of his pick. Also the awful moment when in an excess of zeal he built the Major a canvas chair, which collapsed immediately he sat in it, thereby condemning my irate commanding officer to walk in a bent-up position with the framework attached to his person, till his howls of rage produced deliverance. But time is short, and the pegs are small. He was just one of the Robert Browns, that's all ; and the last peg in the lad's life is perhaps the smallest of all.

It was wet two or three days ago, very wet ; and I, as usual, had gone out without a mackintosh. We were away back west of Ypres, in a region generally considered safe. It is safe as a matter of fact by comparison, but occasionally the Hun treats us to an obus or two—lest we forget his existence. I got back very wet, very angry, and very bored, and howled for Brown. There was no answer, save only from the doctor's orderly, and he it was who told me. Brown had started out when the rain came on, six or seven hours before, with my mackintosh, and, not returning, they had gone to look for him.

In a ditch they found him with the water dyed crimson, a few minutes before he died. It was just a stray shell that found its mark on the lad. I can see him in my mind stumping along the road, humming his song— and then, without warning, the sudden screech close on top of him, the pitiful, sagging knees, the glazing film of death, with none to aid him through as he had helped that other, for the road was little used.

Thank God! they found him before the end, but he only made one remark. " I couldn't get no farther, Dick," he muttered, " but the mack ain't stained."

I went up to see him in the brewery where they'd carried him, and I looked on his honest, ugly face for the last time. " The mack ain't stained." No, lad, it isn't. May I, when I come to the last fence, be able to say the same.

Though he spoke it literally, there is, methinks, a man's religion in those last words of
Robert Brown, Driver, R.E., and sometime
batman.

THE COWARD

TOUT COMPRENDRE C'EST TOUT PARDONNER

JAMES DAWLISH'S soul was sick within him.
His tongue was cleaving to the roof of his
mouth, parched and dry ; his eyes gazed
dully out of his white face at the pack of
the man in front of him, who, like himself
and fifty others, crouched huddled up in the
ditch beside the road. Away in front
stretched the pavé road, gleaming white in
the dim light of dusk, the road that ran
straight, as only French roads can, until,
topping the rise three-quarters of a mile
ahead, it merged into the darkness of the
two lines of trees that guarded it. And
twenty yards beyond that rise lay the German
lines.

Then suddenly it came again. Out of the
silent evening air the sudden salvo of six
sharp hisses and six deafening cracks, the
angry zipping of high explosive shrapnel
through the trees over his head, the little

eddies of dust in the road, the little thuds in the banks of the ditch where he crouched. Put baldly—in the language of the army— the Germans were searching the road with whizz-bangs, and had being doing so for twenty minutes. And the soul of James Dawlish was sick within him.

All around him men were muttering, laughing, cursing, each after his kind. In front an officer, very young, very new, was speaking to his sergeant-major. What he said is immaterial—which is perhaps as well, as he did nothing but repeat himself. The sergeant-major was a man of understanding, grown as used to shells as man may grow. For that matter so had the others—they were not a new regiment. James Dawlish was not new either. It was not his baptism of fire—he'd been shelled many times before ; but for all that he was afraid—terribly, horribly afraid.

The psychology of fear is a strange thing. It is perhaps paradoxical, but I venture to think that without fear there can be no bravery—bravery, that is, in the true sense of the word. There are, I believe, some men who are without fear—literally and absolutely fearless. Such a condition of mind may be induced by sincere fatalism, but I rather think in the majority of cases it is due to a peculiar and fortunate twist of the brain. Inasmuch as one man will without thought dive forty feet into the sea and enjoy it, so will another, whose limbs would tremble at such a thought, boldly enter a cage of lions. Temperament, temperament only, at the bottom of it. And so it may well be that, were the wonderful, soul-stirring heroism of some V.C. to be weighed in the balance of mind and soul rather than in the balance of deed, he would be found less worthy to hold that coveted ribbon than a man whose sole contribution to fame was that he didn't run away.

Not so James Dawlish. With him fear seemed to be cumulative. Each time he came under fire, his terror of it increased. With most of us, who lay no claim to be without fear, sooner or later a merciful callousness settles down. Not that, if we think about it, our dislike of the *genus obus* is any less—far from it. But as time goes on, and a man does not get hit, though one day the dug-out he had just left was flattened by a crump, and another the man he was talking to was killed before his eyes ; though he may have had a hundred narrow escapes, yet in time it becomes to a greater or less extent his natural element—a part and parcel of his life—a thing of routine as much as breakfast, more so, in some cases. But that man is no braver now than he was : more fearless, perhaps, but no braver. It is, then, with most of us, the factor of custom that pulls us through the mill, and preserves our reason.

But to James Dawlish that factor was denied. Fate had decreed that the brain of James Dawlish should be so fashioned that no immunity from death in the past should detract one iota from the hideous terror of death in the present. Every tour of duty in the trenches he died a thousand deaths. He saw himself left dying between the lines, stabbed in a sudden German rush, the recipient of the attentions of a Black Maria. He pictured to himself countless forms of death, each one more unpleasant than the last. Only the routine, the discipline of the army had held him up to date, that and the complete lack of opportunity to run away.

It is easier said than done to run away from the front-line trenches, especially when things are quiet.

Which all boils down to the one essential fact that James Dawlish was a coward in the true sense of the word. Hundreds of men have lost their nerve temporarily, hundreds of men, huddled in a scratch in the ground, with their senses deadened and crushed by an inferno of bursting shells, have done things which the thoughtless dub cowardly. Men suddenly exposed to gas with no means of protection, men waking to find the trench full of liquid fire, these and countless other cases no man may judge unless he has stood beside them in similar circumstances and not been found wanting. But James Dawlish was not one of these. To him every moment of his life was a living death, a torture worse than hell. If one looks back to the cause of things, it was, I suppose, his misfortune and not his fault. He had been made so. Fear was a part of him, and pity rather than contempt is perhaps the fairest feeling to entertain for him. He could no more help his state of permanent terror, than a cat can help its dislike of water.

" Get up." The word came down the line, the shelling seemed to have stopped. The men in front of him were moving off up the road, but still he remained. A man tripped over him and cursed, but James Dawlish sat fumbling with his putties. No scheme was in his head ; he had no intention of not going up to the front line ; but clear out of the jumble of thoughts in his brain was his feverish desire to postpone if only for five minutes his nearer acquaintance with those great green flares that lobbed into the sky so near him. He could almost hear the faint hiss as they fell burning to the ground. God ! how he hated it ! Then they started shelling a cross-road a hundred yards behind him, and he cowered still closer in the ditch, almost whimpering—for it had suddenly struck him that he was alone. His platoon had gone on and left him : he had not even got the faint comfort of another man beside him. He was alone, utterly alone on a shell-swept road with an occasional spare bullet pinging down it, and the trees throwing fantastic shadows around him.

Then suddenly above his head he heard voices, and the soft thrumming of a motor.

" They'll stop hating in a moment and then we'll rush it," said a voice.

James Dawlish looked up, and in that moment the idea was born in his bemused brain. Safety—away from those cursed shells —away from those hissing green flares! What matter the right or wrong—what matter the penalties ? Nothing entered into his calculations, saving only the thought of escape. And so with infinite caution he got out of the ditch and approached the driver of the ambulance as if he had been coming down the road.

" Give us a lift, mate, will you ? " he asked casually.

" Right ho ! hop in. They've stopped shelling." The ambulance was off—the driver unsuspicious. Many isolated men walk about behind the trenches at night, and anyway, it was none of his business.

Thus it came about that No. 1234 Private James Dawlish, of the second battalion of the Loamshires, when on active service, deserted His Majesty's Forces.

.   .   .   .   .

Now Thomas Atkins alone in a strange country, despite all rumours to the contrary, is a somewhat helpless individual. He will generally contrive to feed himself, and he has an infallible instinct for spotting those estaminets that contain the unpleasing liquid which passes as beer in Flanders. But when it comes to getting from one place to another, he gives up the unequal contest, and throws himself on the mercy of the nearest officer. And this was precisely what James Dawlish could not do. In the first place, he didn't know where he did want to go ; he didn't much care so long as he kept out of the trenches ; and in the second place, he was quite an old enough soldier to realise what he had done and, what was far more to the point, to realise the penalty. " Death or such less punishment as is in this Act mentioned."

Detection, he knew, would not come from the regiment. Too many men are reported missing for his absence to evoke any awkward questions. It was the people behind he had to fear, military police, assistant provost-marshals, and such-like abominations to the evil-doer. If only he could lie hid for a time, and finally borrow some one else's clothes and disappear—that was his half-formed play. Hazy and nebulous, true—but

9

anything, anything on God's earth rather than go back.

It was while he was turning it over in his mind, with no clear idea of where he was going, that, rounding a bend in the road, he saw a few miles off the monastery that is set on a hill, and which forms one of the few noticeable landmarks in Flanders. The monastery where the cavalry had a skirmish in October last, and the monks in their brown cowls and cassocks buried the result. There were English troopers, and German Uhlans, and also there was a German Prince. And this monastery, set on the Mont des Cats, came back to James Dawlish as an old friend. Had he not billeted in the village at the foot of it with the unpronounceable name when he first came to the front ?

No need now to ask his way—he would go back to the village—where there was a girl he knew of, and she would help him. And so with a comparatively light heart he started, and in the course of a few hours he found himself at the farm which had been his first resting-place in France.

Now, it is quite possible that, were it not for the extraordinary paucity of girls whom one

may look at without smoked glasses in this
delectable country, James Dawlish might
have staved off the inevitable for quite a
time.   When he left the ambulance, he had
carefully buried in a pond his rifle and equipment, and anyone meeting him strolling down
the road would have taken him to be merely a
man from a unit resting.   To make things
more sure, he had removed his cap badge,
and the titles on his shoulder straps.   There
was nothing whatever to show what he be-
longed to ; he was merely a disreputable atom
of the big machine in much-damaged khaki.
But, as I have said, there was a girl in the
case, and moreover, she was a girl who had
been very kind to James Dawlish earlier in
the proceedings.   She really had been quite
fond of him, but when he went away and the
place knew him no more, being a girl of common sense she transferred her attentions to
his successor.   As a matter of fact, there
had been several successors, as regiments
came and went, the intervals being filled with
the semi-permanent sheet-anchor who stood
for several hours each day at the cross-roads
by the church in the village with the unpronounceable name.   And this sheet-anchor,

who watched men come and watched men go, was a corporal in the Military Police.

It was during one of his innings with the fair maiden that James Dawlish tactlessly arrived on the scene; and when the Corporal made his appearance in the evening, having successfully carried out his arduous duties regulating the traffic during the afternoon he found the object of his affections planted firmly in the arms of an extremely untidy and travel-stained private. It is perhaps unnecessary to state that, annoyed as the Corporal was at this untoward intrusion on his preserves, his feelings were harmonious compared to those of Private Dawlish. To run full tilt into a Red Cap—as Tommy calls them—was the last thing he had intended doing; and a glance at the Corporal's face told him that the Corporal was out for blood.

" Who the 'ell are you, and what's your regiment ? " he remarked tersely, looking at his badgeless cap.

And James Dawlish knew the game was up. He didn't even know what regiments were in the neighbourhood ; if he had he might have lied and tried a bluff. So he said who he was, and named his regiment.

" The Loamshires ? " said the Corporal.
" Second battalion ? But they're in the
trenches, for my brother's in that there battalion." The Military Policeman looked at
him mercilessly. " What are you doing 'ere,
my lad ? "

And this time James Dawlish was silent :
there was nothing to say. To an officer he'd
have lied, uselessly, perhaps, but lied on
principle : to a corporal he knew the futility.
Two minutes later the door closed behind
them, and they passed down the street.

Thus it came about that No. 1234, Private
James Dawlish, of the second battalion of
the Loamshires, was apprehended by the
Military Police, and placed in the guard-room
of the village with the unpronounceable name,
to await the investigation of his case by the
A.P.M. or assistant provost-marshal of the
district.

.   .   .   .   .

And now the inevitable end must be written.
There is not much to tell ; the whole thing was
plain. The A.P.M. investigated the case, and
it stood revealed in its hideous bareness.
There was not a single redeeming feature. It
was no case of a man's nerve temporarily

breaking under some fearful strain : where now, in the wisdom of those in high places, a man may work off his slur, by returning and trying again. It was just a simple case of cowardice and desertion in the presence of the enemy, and for it there was no excuse. That James Dawlish was made that way may have been his misfortune, but if that were taken as an excuse a good many men might find themselves sitting quietly in villages with unpronounceable names, while their pals lost their lives further east.

So in due course James Dawlish stood before a court-martial. The evidence was heard, and then the accused was marched out, ignorant of his fate.

" The Court is closed to consider its finding." Thus spoke the President, a Major in the infantry. And when the door had closed, he turned to the junior member—a subaltern of gunners—and his face was grave. It is the law of courts-martial that the junior member gives his idea of the adequate sentence first, in order that he may not be influenced by what his seniors have said.

" What is your opinion ? " asked the Major. The subaltern drummed on the table with his fingers, and stared in front of him. Death, or such less penalty. The words seemed stamped on the wall. For a space he was silent ; then he swallowed twice and spoke.

The Major glanced at the Captain, and the Captain, who was gazing fixedly out of the window, turned slowly round, and nodded. " I agree," he remarked incisively.

The Major looked at the papers in front of him, and mechanically produced his cigarette case. Then he wrote, and his hand shook a little.

And though the Major and the Captain and the subaltern had one and all looked on death many times unmoved, yet that night they were strangely silent.

To those who insist on the hundred and first chapter I can but quote the following bald announcement that appeared in a document of surpassing dullness known as General Routine Orders. It had a number which I forget, and it was sandwiched between an interesting statement about exchanging French money into English, and a still more entrancing one on the subject of the Regimental Debts Act. Moreover, it was labelled Courts-Martial, and ran as follows :

No. 1234, Private James Dawlish, 2nd Battalion, The Loamshires, was tried by a Field General Courts-Martial on the following charge :

" When on active service deserting His Majesty's Service."

The sentence of the Court was " To suffer death by being shot."

The sentence was duly carried out at 4 a.m. on August 3rd.

. . . . .

And the only thing which gives a man to think is that about six hours after they laid that poor dishonoured clay in the ground, the manager of a large emporium at home was pleased to promote one of his shopwalkers from the glove department to a sphere of activity which concerned itself principally with stockings. I don't know why stockings were more highly paid than gloves in that emporium, but no matter.

The point of the thing is the shopwalker. His name is Dawlish—Augustus Dawlish. He used to look down on his brother James. Soldiering is not a genteel occupation compared to selling stockings. I suppose he'll do so still more if he ever learns the truth.

EBENEEZER THE GOAT

NO GOAT BY ANY OTHER NAME E'ER SMELT AS MUCH

DRIVER ROBERT BROWN, as I have already remarked, was an admirable man in many ways. And I have frequently observed to other members of the mess, that one of the things that most endeared him to me was his love of animals.

Brown was not a beauty, I admit: his face was of the general-utility order, and he had a partiality for singing a dreadful song of which he only knew one line—at least that is all we ever heard, thank Heaven! At cockcrow, 'neath the midday sun, at eventide, did he foist upon a long-suffering world, with a powerful and somewhat flat voice, the following despairing wail : " What a faice, what a faice, what a norrible faice, lumme, what a faice she 'ad." Occasional streams of invective issued from neighbouring dug-outs. The result was immaterial;

he merely appraised other portions of the
lady's anatomy. Once I remember the cook
was ill; Brown did his work. He was a
good lad—he always did every one else's
work. We were hungry—very hungry—and
he, stout fellow, was preparing our repast.

" Homlette, sir," he had murmured con-
fidentially, " peas and taters, and fresh
meat ! " and with his honest face shining
with eagerness to prepare this Epicurean
banquet he had gone about his business.
The shadows lengthened—an appetising smell
greeted our nostrils ; we forgave him his untoward references to his adored one's " faice."
Then it happened.

" What a neye, what a neye, what a norrible
heye, lumme "—there was a fearful pause and
a sizzling noise—" lumme, the whole perishing homlette's in the fire." It was ; and in
a gallant attempt at rescue he upset the
meat in an adjacent stagnant pool. The
only thing we got were the peas, and they
rattled on the tin plates like shrapnel bullets.

However, as I've said several times, he
was an admirable lad, and a love of animals
atoned for a multitude of sins. At least
every one thought so, until he adopted a

goat. It was an animal of unprepossessing aspect and powerful smell—very powerful. I speak with some authority on the subject of goats, for in the course of my service I have lived for a space on an abominable island " set in a sapphire sea." Ninety per cent. of its population are goats, the remainder priests ; and without intermission, in a ceaseless stream, the savour of that island flows upwards and outwards. I therefore claim to speak with authority, and Brown's goat would have held its own with ease in any community.

He accommodated it in a special dug-out, from which it habitually escaped ; generally at full speed just as the Major was passing. When the Major had been knocked down twice, Brown was accorded an interview. It was a breezy little affair, that interview, and Brown for some hours seemed a trifle dazed. For some time after he was busy in the goat's dug-out, and when I passed on my way out to a job of work that evening, I found him contemplating his handiwork with pride. Not content with doubling its head-rope, he had shackled the goat fore and aft to pegs in the ground—one fore-leg and one hind-leg

being secured by rope to two pegs firmly
driven into the floor of the dug-out.

" That's done you, my beauty," I heard
him murmuring ; and then he relapsed into
his song, while the goat watched him pen-
sively out of one eye.

I subsequently discovered that it was
about three o'clock next morning it happened. The goat, having slipped its collar
and pulled both pegs, shot from its dug-out
with a goat-like cry of joy. Then the pegs
alarmed it, dangling from its legs—and it
went mad. At least, that's what the Major
said. It appeared that, having conducted
an exhaustive survey of a portion of the line
with the General and his staff, they had returned to refresh weary nature with a portion
of tongue and a bottle of fine old port—the
old and bold, full of crustiness. Hardly had
they got down to it, when, with a dreadful
and earsplitting noise, the goat bounded
through the door of the dug-out. One peg
flying round caught the General on the knee,
the other wrapped itself round the leg of the
table. The old gentleman, under the impression that the Germans had broken
through, drew his revolver, and with a great

cry of " Death rather than dishonour,"
discharged his weapon six times into the
blue.   Mercifully there were no casualties,
as the staff, with great presence of mind, had
hurled themselves flat on their faces during
this dangerous proceeding.   Each shot came
to rest in the crate containing the whisky,
and the fumes from the liquid which flowed
over the floor so excited the goat that with one
awful effort it broke loose and disappeared
into an adjacent cornfield.   I cannot vouch
for all this—in fact the mess as a body received
the story coldly.   The junior subaltern even
went so far as to murmur to another graceless
youth that it was one way of accounting
for eight bottles of whisky and two of port—
and that it was very creditable to all concerned that they said it was a goat, and not a
spotted megothaurus.   All I can vouch for
is that when the Major woke up the next
day, he issued an ultimatum.   The goat must
go—alive if possible ; dead if necessary—but
if he ever again saw the accursed beast, he,
personally, would destroy it with gun-cotton.
As he really seemed in earnest about the
matter, I decided that something must be
done.   I sent for Brown.

" Brown," I said when he appeared, " the goat must go."

" What, Hebeneezer, sir ? " he answered in dismay.

" I do not know its name," I returned firmly, " and I was under the impression that it was a female ; but if you call it Ebeneezer, then Ebeneezer must go." He became pensive. " Dead or alive that accursed mammal must depart, never to return. It has already seriously injured the Major's constitution."

" It has, sir ? " There was a world of surprise in his tone. " Of course, it don't do to go playing about with it, or crossing it like, but——"

" The goat has done the crossing. Twice —at full speed."

" 'E seems a bit quiet this morning, sir. Off his food like. And e's lost a bit of 'is tail." Brown scratched his head meditatively.

The fact did not surprise me—but I preserved a discreet silence. " Get rid of it this morning, and see that it never returns ! " I ordered, and the incident closed—at least I thought so at the time.

Brown reported his departure that evening, and with a sigh of relief from the Major the odoriferous Ebeneezer was struck off the strength with effect from that day's date. It is true that I noticed strange and mysterious absences on the part of my servant when he left carrying something in paper and returned empty-handed, and that in the back of my mind I had a vague suspicion that somewhere in the neighbourhood there still remained that evil-smelling animal looked after and fed by Robert Brown. But, as a week passed and we saw and smelt the beast no more, my suspicions were lulled to rest, and I dismissed the untoward incident from my mind. I am always of an optimistic disposition !

I should say it was about ten days after Ebeneezer's departure that I awoke one morning early to the sound of a violent altercation without.

" I tells you, you can't see the Major. 'E's in 'is bath." Peering out, I saw Brown and the cook warding off two extremely excited Belgians.

" Bath ! Bath ! *Qu'est que c'est*—bath ! " The stouter Belgian gesticulated freely.

" You are—vot you say—*du génie, n'est-ce-pas* ? Eet is important—ver important that I see monsieur le commandant."

" Look here, cully," murmured the cook, removing a clay pipe from his mouth and expectorating with great accuracy ; " moosoo le commondant is in 'is bath—see. You'll 'ave to wait. Bath—savez. Eau." He pointed to a bucket of water.

" *Mon Dieu !* " shuddered the Belgian. " *Eh bien ! mon ami*, ees zere anozer officer ? It is *très important*." He was getting excited again. " *Les Boches*—zere is a *bruit* under ze earth—*comprenez* ? Zey make a—oh ! ze word, ze word—zey make *une mine*, and zen we all go Pouff ! " He waved his hands to Heaven.

" Mean. Mean," remarked the cook contemplatively. " Wot the deuce does he mean ? Anyway, Bob, we might take 'im on as a sparklet machine."

Then I thought it was about time I came to the rescue. "What's all the trouble, Brown?" I asked, coming out of the dug-out.

" These 'ere blokes, sir . . ." he began ; but as both Belgians began talking at once, he got no further.

" Ah ! monsieur," they cried, " *vous êtes du génie ?* " I assured them I was of the engineers. " Then come *vite, s'il vous plait.* We are of ze artillery, and ze Germans zey make *une mine, n'est-ce-pas ?* We go up Pouff. Our guns zey go up Pouff—*aussi.*"

" Mining," I cried, " the Germans mining here ! Impossible, messieurs. Why, we're a mile and a half behind the firing-line." I regret to say I was a little peevish.

Nevertheless they assured me it was so— not once, but many times. Strange noises, they affirmed, were heard in the bowels of the earth near their battery—mysterious rumblings occurred ; they continually assured me they were going Pouff !

I went to the Major. He was not in a good temper—he rarely is in the early morning—and the last blade of his safety razor was blunt.

" Mining here ! " he barked. " What the deuce are they talking about ? It's probably nesting time for woodpeckers or something. Oh ! yes—go away and see," in reply to my question. " Anything to get those two embryo volcanoes off the premises : and don't let 'em come back, for Heaven's sake ! "

10

So I went. Undoubtedly there were noises —very strange subterranean noises, in front of that battery. Moreover, the sounds seemed to come from different places. At times they were very loud ; at others they ceased. The excitement soon became intense. Stout officers lay all over the ground with their ears pressed in the mud. The commandant of the battery ran round in small circles saying Pouff ! distractedly. In fact every one said Pouff ! to every one else. It became the password of the morning. Then at last the crucial moment arrived. The centre of the storm, so to speak, had been located—the place where, so far as we could tell, the noise seemed consistently loudest. At that point the Belgians started to dig ; and instantly a triumphant shout rent the air. The place was an old disused shaft, boarded over and covered with a thin layer of earth. At last it was open, and from it there issued loud and clear a dreadful tapping.

" A network of galleries," cried an interpreter excitedly. " Probably old shafts reaching the German lines. We are lost." He and the commandant had a pouffing match in their despair. But now the noise became greater, and we heard distinctly a human voice. It was at that moment the dread suspicion first dawned on me. An army of men hung over the edge, armed to the teeth with pistols and bowie knives, tin cans and bits of brick. Tap, tap, louder and louder, came the noise. The Pouffers were silent—every one breathed hard.

Then suddenly I heard it echoing along the hollow gallery : " What a faice, what a faice, what a norrible faice—Hebeneezer, you perisher ; where the 'ell are you ?—lumme, what a faice she 'ad."

" ' The Watch on the Rhine.' They sing their accursed song," howled the commandant. " Belgium for ever, *mes braves !* "

It was at that moment that a stout spectator, moved to frenzy by this appeal, or else owing to a rush of blood to the head, hurled his tin can. Every one fired—a ghastly noise rent the gloom of the well ; there was the sound of something departing at a great rate ; a heavy fall ; and then silence.

I walked thoughtfully back to my dug-out, refusing the offer of making further explorations. As I passed inside I met Brown. He was limping, and the skin was off his nose."

" What have you been doing ? " I demanded.

" I fell down, sir," he answered.

" Brown," I said sternly, " where is the goat, Ebeneezer ? "

Brown rubbed his nose and looked thoughtfully at me. " Well, sir, I can't say as 'ow I rightly know. 'E *was*——" Further disclosures were nipped in the bud by the sudden appearance of the Major. He was inarticulate with rage.

" Get me my revolver," he spluttered. " Get me my revolver. That damn goat's come back and knocked me down again ! "

But Brown had discreetly vanished.

THE PEPNOTISED MILK

AUNT A. IS NOT HER NAME , BUT I CAN
VOUCH FOR THE PEPNOTISED MILK, TO SAY
NOTHING OF THE MOTH BALLS

AUNT ARAMINTA is one of the dearest souls
that ever breathed. I may say at once that
she is not my aunt—rather does she belong
to a subaltern of the unit. But we all feel
a sort of proprietary right to Aunt Araminta.
In the past she has supplied us all with many
things. During the winter we received frequent consignments of cholera belts and
socks, gloves and khaki handkerchiefs. Most
of them had moth balls sewn in. I have
never seen her, but I unhesitatingly state
that she is of the moth-ball type—she is a
martyr to them. This conclusion is confirmed by her nephew—a graceless youth.
Now I regret to say that much of our affection for the elderly Araminta has gone. It
may return in time—but she has been directly
responsible for our being sent to the front-
line trenches when we were enjoying a comparative rest on a somewhat safer line. No

doubt she was actuated by the best intentions in the world, but just at present we don't mention her if the Major is about.

It all occurred owing to a shortage of milk —condensed or otherwise. We were on a line, which though safe—or more or less so— did not admit of our obtaining the genuine article with any ease. I appealed to Driver Robert Brown, our sheet-anchor—our Admirable Crichton. He it is who buys us eggs ; he gets us bread and pork chops ; anon he obtains tinned salmon mingled with sardines. Once he essayed some fizzy water —Eau Gazeuse is, I believe, the correct name. Something got mixed, and the mess lowered a dozen Apenta before retiring to bed. However, that is another story.

Into the ears then of this our guide and mentor, our home within a home, our ever-ready gas cooker, I whispered the word milk. He said he knew of a cow, and he'd see what could be done.

Soon after he left with a tin receptacle and an air of determination ; an hour after he returned with neither. He retired into the cook-house, and shortly after there came voices in wordy warfare.

" You mean to say you ain't got no milk ? " demanded the cook aggrievedly.

" No—I ain't." Brown emerged and mopped his brow wearily.

" Couldn't you find the cow ? I told you where it was." The Doctor's orderly ceased placing chloride of lime on the tomb of a rat. " And wot 'ave you done to your face ? It's 'orrible. Worse than usual."

" Less about my face." Brown's retort was a trifle heated. " I tells you, when I got to that there place you told me of—you couldn't see the perishing cow for the crowd. There was a row of blokes with mess tins, and one of 'em 'ad a dixie. When it come to my turn, I sits down by the old girl, and puts the tin on the floor. I got one jet going for about five seconds and that missed the blooming bucket. Then she shut up, and not another drop could I get. A perisher in the gunners, 'e says, ' Pull 'arder,' 'e says, ' Great strength returns the penny.' So I got down to it like, just to wake 'er up, when blowed if she didn't 'op it. 'Opped it, and kicked me in the faice as a souvenir." He felt the injured member tenderly.

" I don't know as 'ow I notice much the

matter with it." The cook gazed impassively at Brown's face. " It looks just like it always did, worse luck. But then it ain't the sort of face as is affected by little things like that. As the medical profession observed it is a norrible thing—your face. Ain't it, Bob ? "

This appeal for confirmation to the face's owner touched me greatly. However, as I am quite unable to record the answer—and the rest of the conversation does not call for comment—I will pass on to the moment when I mentioned the shortage of condensed milk, and the failure up to the present to supply the genuine to an indignant mess. I may mention—*en passant*—that in a moment of imbecility I had permitted myself to be thrust into the position of mess caterer. The Doctor used to do it—but he fell in love, and was unable to do anything but play " Somewhere a Voice is Calling " on the gramophone. As the record was cracked, there was a general feeling of relief when the junior subaltern strafed a mouse with it. However, the doctor being beyond human help, his mantle descended on me. I was away when it did so—but that is by the way. The result would probably have been the same. Brown, as I have said, did it all; but I was the figure head—on me descended the wrath of outraged officers compelled to eat sardines past their first youth, and the scene after the little episode of the Apenta water was quite dreadful.

"Why not go yourself and milk the bally cow if Brown can't?" remarked one of them unfeelingly. "Sing to it, dearie—one of those little love ballads of your early youth. Something is bound to occur."

And then up spake Horatius—it *is* his name—he being the one that owned Aunt Araminta. "The old girl has just written me asking me if we want anything. I'll tell her to send some condensed along. Of course it won't be here for some time—but it's better than nothing." He turned over the last sheet. "She is sending a hamper, as a matter of fact. Perhaps there'll be some in it."

"Two to one it's nothing but moth balls," remarked the doctor irreverently. "Heavens! do you remember the time the old dear got one mixed up in her home-made potted meat—and the Major broke his tooth on it."

.   .   .   .   .

It was the next day that parcel arrived. A shower of white balls descended to the floor, two odd socks, some peppermint bull's-eyes, a letter, and *the* bottle.

"Great Heavens!" muttered Horatius, gingerly inspecting the collection. "What has the old girl sent?" He opened the letter, read it, and asked for whiskey.

"My dear nephew," he read, in a hushed voice. "I am sending you a bottle of the new milk—Dr. Trapheim's Pepnotised Milk. As you will gather from perusing the label on the bottle, it is a marvellous discovery. At first I feared from the inventor's name that he might be of Germanic extraction, but subsequent inquiries enabled me to discover that he is in reality the son of a Swedish Jew who married a girl from Salt Lake City. So, of course, he must be all right.

"In this wonderful milk, my dear nephew, there are three million germs to the cubic foot—or is it inch? I forget which. Anyway, a very large number of nutritious germs exist in it. You remember poor Pluto?

" The pug," he explained hoarsely, and continued reading.

" Regularly for a week before his death he drank a saucerful each night—and it eased him wonderfully. You remember his dreadful asthma. It quite left him, and he would lie for hours without movement after drinking it.

" I hastened to buy a bottle—and send it to you all, with my very best wishes,

" Your affectionate

" AUNT ARAMINTA."

" P.S.—It may have different effects on different people. The cook, silly girl, has given notice."

And for a space there was silence. Then Horatius picked up the bottle, and in a hushed voice recited the label.

" Cures consumption, eradicates eczema, intimidates itch, and routs rabies. Makes bonny bouncing babies." He choked slightly, and passed it on to me. There was nothing that milk wouldn't do. Its effect on the human system was like rare wine, only permanent. It caused a clarity of vision, an improvement in intellect, a brightening of brain that started with the first bottle drank, and increased and multiplied with every succeeding bottle. It enlarged the bust in one paragraph, and removed double chins in another. Old and young alike thrived on it— it was the world's masterpiece in health-giving foods. Moreover it was impossible to tell it from ordinary milk when drinking it. That was its great charm. It could be used in tea or coffee or drunk neat. It made no odds. After one sip you bagged a winner. The betting was about a fiver to a dried banana skin that after a bottle you became a sort of superman.

It was while we were sitting a little dazedly with the bottle occupying a position of honour in the centre of the dug-out that we heard the Major's voice outside—also the General's, to say nothing to two staff officers. They had walked far and fast, and I gathered from the conversation that *Percy the pip-squeak*—gun, small, Hun variety—had thrust himself upon them. Their tempers did not seem all that one could desire. The prevalent idea, moreover, appeared to be tea.

"We'd better decant it, in a jar," said Horatius gloomily. "The General loathes tea without milk, and it says on the bottle you can't tell the difference."

The Doctor, however, was firm. He refused to allow anyone to drink it without being told, and as he pointed out if you tell a distinctly warm and irritable old gentleman that the apparently harmless liquid he sees in an ordinary jug on the table is in reality a pepnotised breed with three million germs to the cubic inch in it—he will probably not be amused, but will send you back to the trenches as a dangerous individual.

Horatius pointed out still more gloomily that to offer the old gentleman a bottle which expressly set out to eradicate eczema and intimidate itch was an even less likely way to his favour.

The General's entrance at that moment, however, settled the matter, and we began tea. It was not a cheerful meal to start with— rather the reverse. In fact, when I had explained and apologised for the absence of any milk, and introduced the bottle to the meeting, the atmosphere of the dug-out resembled a lawyer's office when the relatives hear their aunt's money has been left to a society for providing cannibals with unshrinkable wool underclothes.

" Who sent the damn stuff ? " asked the Major coldly.

"Aunt Araminta." Horatius nervously removed the wire that held in the cork. One of the staff officers carefully picked up the bottle and proceeded to read the label, while the General's expression was that of a man who gazes at short range into the mouth of a gun.

" It's wonderful stuff," continued Horatius. " Roll, bowl, or pitch, you bag a coconut every time you drink it. My aunt, sir, speaks most highly of it." He turned to the General, who received the news without enthusiasm.

" Three million bugs to the cubic inch," read the staff officer musingly. " And if there are twenty cubic inches in the bottle, we get sixty million bugs. Allowing for casualties, and in order to be on the safe side in case the makers swindled, call it fifty million."

" I think," remarked the General, breaking an oppressive silence, " I will have a whiskey and soda."

It was at that moment I noticed the cork. My shout of warning came too late. With great force and a noise like a black Maria, it flew from the bottle, and from point-blank range imbedded itself in the General's left eye. The entire mess became covered with a species of white foam, but the General took the brunt. For a moment there was a dreadful silence, and then with a wild shout we hurled ourselves through the doorway. I have smelt many smells in many cities : I have stood outside tallow works. I have lived in the salient of Ypres. I have—but why elaborate ? I say it with solemnity and earnestness : I have never smelt anything like that milk ? Never in my wildest moments have I imagined that such a smell could exist. It was superhuman, stupendous, wonderful.

The General, who had lost his eye-glass in the excitement and then trodden on it, was running round in small circles, holding his nose. He was unable at any time to see with his right eye, and a portion of cork still remained in his left. Without cessation he trumpeted for assistance.

" Wipe it off," he howled. " Wipe the

damn stuff off, you fatheaded idiots." He fell heavily into a Johnson hole, and became temporarily winded.

From all directions men were emerging with helmets on, thinking a new form of gas had been evolved by the Hun. A neighbouring doctor, seeing the General in a recumbent position, rushed up to render assistance, while two staff officers, assisted by the Major, made gingerly dabs at the old gentleman with handkerchiefs.

At last it was over. The cork plucked from his eye, he arose and in splendid isolation confronted us. After swallowing hard once or twice, he spoke.

" I do not know if this was a jest." His voice was hoarse. " My eye-glass is broken, the sight of my other eye irreparably damaged. I am now going to Corps Headquarters, and provided the Corps Commander can sit in the same room with that cursed woman's fifty million stinking bacilli, I propose to ask him to let you try them at once on the Germans."

Amidst a solemn hush he departed—with two staff officers at a discreet distance. I gather that the spectacle of their departure by car, with the one who'd failed to get the seat next the driver sitting on the step at the side, and the General enthroned alone like a powerful-smelling fungoidal growth, was not the least pathetic incident of the afternoon.

But Aunt A. is not popular.

WILL YOU TAKE OVER HIS HORSE, SIR ?

TO A PAL.   NOVEMBER, 1914.   R.I.P.

IN the sky overhead the sun struggled through the drifting clouds, throwing a watery gleam on the sea of mud which called itself the picket line.   Just for a moment it seemed as if it would triumph, and, as I looked up, the old bay horse with the batman standing at his head was bathed in sunshine.   Behind him the troop horses steadily munching hay ; the men in little scattered groups squatting round camp fires watching their dinners cook. Just the same as it was yesterday, just the same as it was the day before, but—" Will you take over his horse, sir ? "

.   .   .   .   .

In the distance a black speck seemed to be hanging in the air.   All round it little sharp flashes of fire and fleecy puffs of smoke showed that the Germans had also seen that speck and hoped it was within range.   There was one complete set of six smoke balls, so close together that one could almost cover them with a soup plate. Another set had only five. Ah! there was the sixth, a little wide. There had been three perfect groups of six when he and I had been looking at the same thing a few mornings before. Listlessly I watched the black speck. Gradually it grew larger and larger until the big biplane passed overhead. And underneath the Union Jack—painted on the plane. Just the same, thank Heaven, just the same. The flag untouched, each unit which represents that flag carrying on the inexorable work. There is no cessation ; there are others ; it is war, but—" Will you take over his horse ? "

.   .   .   .   .

The old bay horse ! I wonder if you, too, remember that day at Tattersall's. Do you remember the hand running over your legs and stopping at that big splint on your off fore ? Can you hear again that voice you've got to know so well ? " Look at those hocks, man ; look at that shoulder ; that splint may just bring him down to my price." And do you remember the hunts ? Do you

remember that point-to-point when you both
came such a crumpler at that big stake and
binder ? Perhaps you remember, old horse,
perhaps you do ; for who shall say just
where an animal's knowledge begins and ends?
There's no good your looking round like that.
You haven't seen him this morning, have
you ?—and you know something's wrong,
but you don't know what. How should
you ? You don't understand, and I do,
Heaven knows—which is worse. In time
perhaps the sugar will taste just as good out
of my hand as far as you're concerned. I
hope it will, because—well, you heard the
question, too—" Will you take over his
horse ? "

.   .   .   .   .

Yes, I must take you over until someone
else can take you from me, if you come
through this show alive. You don't know
much about that someone, do you, old chap ?
Do you remember that day when you made
such a fool of yourself because a side saddle
had been put on you for the first time, and
your master with a sack round his waist was
sitting on your back all askew, as you thought,

And then about a week after, when you were quite accustomed to it, someone else got upon you who was so light that you scarcely felt any weight at all.   And when you lifted your heels a bit, just for fun, because you hardly knew there was anyone there at all, do you remember how he rubbed your muzzle and talked to you until you became quiet ? But there are so many things that you can't know, aren't there, old horse ?   You weren't in my room when he came round to it that night to tell me before anyone else of his wonderful luck.   You couldn't know that the little light load you carried so often was the most precious thing in the whole world to the man who never missed coming round to your box after dinner on a hunting day, to make sure you were rugged up and bedded down for the night all right.   That's where I get the pull of you, old man.   You see, I was going to be his best man when he could afford to get married.   He insisted on that when he told me first.   But—things have happened since that night, and I'm going to take you over, because I want to give you back to her.   I don't expect you'll carry her hunting again ; women aren't made that

way—at least not this one. Though he'd
like it, I know.

. . . . .

But then, he won't be able to tell her.
That's the rub. I know it was only yesterday
afternoon you heard him say that it was a
grand day for a hunt. I know it was only
last night that you were saddled up suddenly
with all the other troop horses and trotted for
two hours along muddy roads in the darkness.
Then he dismounted—didn't he ?—and went
on on foot with his men, while you and his
other horse stopped behind. And you couldn't
understand why a few hours later, when the
other men mounted, no one got on your
back, and you were led back here. Just a
casual German sniper, sitting in a tree, taking
pot shots into the darkness. Just a small
round hole right in the centre of his forehead
and the back of his head—but we won't
think of that. That's what happened, old
man. Nothing very glorious, nothing at all
heroic. It's so ordinary, isn't it ? It has
already happened hundreds of times. It's
going to happen hundreds more. Everything is going on just the same. It hasn't
made any difference. The guns are in action

just as they were yesterday, and there's
that Maxim going again. But you've lost
your master, old horse ; and I've lost a
friend : and the girl ?——— Not a bad bag,
for half an ounce of lead !

.   .   .   .   .

They've left him up there, with a cross
over his shallow grave, and his name scrawled
on it with an indelible pencil. One can't
get up there in the daylight—it's not safe.
I'd like to have gone to-night to see if it was
all right : but there's a job of work to be
done elsewhere. So I'll have to lie to her.
I'm writing her this afternoon. I can't let
her open the paper one morning, and suddenly
see his name standing out in letters of fire
from all the others. Just a pawn in the
game—another officer killed—a bare, hard
fact, brutal, uncompromising. No more
letters to look forward to : no more socks
and smokes to send out. True, the socks
never fitted, but she didn't know. No : I
can't let her find it out that way. I must
write : though what on earth can I say to
her ? I never could write a letter like that.
If you're going to have your head smashed
with a sledgehammer, one can't do much

to deaden the blow. But I'll tell her I've
seen his grave, and that it's all right. Just
a pawn in the game. Only he was her king.

.   .   .   .   .

" Will you take over his horse, sir ? Your
chestnut is very lame in front."

Teddy, old man, I've hunted with you :
I've shot with you : I've played cricket with
you : I've made love with you. You were
one of Nature's sportsmen : one of the salt
of the earth. May the earth lie lightly on
you, old pal. There's a motor-cyclist coming
with orders now : the same fellow with
spectacles who has been to us for the last
fortnight. There's a Taube overhead, and
the infantry are loosing off at it. It's out of
range, just the same as usual. Everything
is just the same, Teddy, except that someone's
heart has got to be broken, and that I—well,
I've taken over your horse.

THE AFTERMATH

LOOS, OCTOBER, 1915

AWAY in front, gleaming white through the gathering dusk on the side of a hill, lies the front line. Just beyond it, there is another: the Germans. Down in the valley behind that white line a town, from which with monotónous regularity rise great columns of black smoke—German heavies bursting again and again on the crumbling red houses. And from the village there rises a great iron construction with two girdered towers, a landmark for miles. Periodically German crumps sail overhead with a droning noise, woolly bears burst on one's flank, and then a salvo coming unpleasantly near makes one remember that the skyline is not recommended by the best people as a place to stand on, and, getting into the trench, you retire again to the dug-out, to wait for the night to cloak your doings.

In the line of trench are men—men not

there to fight, not even in support. They are there to clear up the battlefield; for only a few days ago the trench in which you are sitting was the German front line. The bed on which you lie has supported a stout Teuton for probably ten long months or more; and now where is he? My predecessor was addicted to the use of a powerful scent of doubtful quality, which still hangs faintly in the air. He also believed in comfort. There are easy chairs, and cupboards, and tables, and, as I say, a bed. Also there are mice, scores of them, who have a great affection for using one's face as a racecourse during one's periods of rest.

But my predecessor was absolutely out of it with another fellow along the trench. His dug-out was a veritable palace, boasting of wall-papers and a carpet, with a decorated dado round the part where dados live, and a pretty design in fruits and birds painted on the ceiling. Bookshelves filled with the latest thing in German wit, and a very nice stove with flue attached. I was beaten by a short head trying to get there, which was, perhaps, as well. Mine confined itself to mice. . . .

Gradually the night falls, and with it starts

the grim task. It was, as I have said, the German line—now it is ours ; the change is not brought about without a price. Turn around, away from that line now almost invisible in front, and look behind. There, over a mass of broken pickets and twisted wire, gleams another white line—our original front trenches. Between you and it lies the no man's land of ten months—and there on that strip of land is part of the price. It lies elsewhere as well, but a patch of fifty yards will serve. There was one, I remember, where the German line had swung out at right angles—a switch—going nearer to ours. In this bit of the line the wire had run perpendicular to the rest of their trench for a few score yards. And in the re-entrant a machine gun had been placed, so that it fired along the wire. The steel casing we found still standing, though the ground around was torn to pieces. That machine gun paid for its construction. . . .

There was one group of four outside, a subaltern and three men. They were lying on the ground, in one close-packed jumble, and the subaltern had his arm around a man's neck. Just in the torn up wire they lay—

the price at the moment of victory. Another five seconds and they would have been in that line ; but it was left to some one else to stop that machine gun firing. And so, beside that motionless, distorted group a hole is dug, and soon no trace remains. One phase of clearing the battlefield ; there are many such holes to be made. A few yards away— this time on the parapet of the trench—a Scotchman and a German are lying together. The Scotchman's bayonet is through the German—his hands still hold the rifle—and as he stabbed him he himself had been shot from behind. A strange tableau : natural enough, yet weirdly grim to the imagination when seen by the dim light two or three days after it took place.

One could elaborate indefinitely. Each of those quiet, twisted figures means some one's tragedy : each of them goes to form the price which must be paid. And at no time, I think, does the brutal realism of war strike home more vividly than when in cold blood one sees before one's eyes the results of what took place in hot blood a few days before. Just a line in the paper—a name— no more. That is the public result of the price, and at one time it seemed to me hard on those behind. Unavoidable of course, but hard. No details—nothing—just a statement. I have changed my mind: there are worse things than ignorance. . . .

Then from the trenches themselves, from the dug-outs, from behind are pulled out the Huns. Caught in their deep dug-outs, with the small, slanting shaft going down to great chambers hewed out of the chalk underneath —and some of the shafts are ten to twelve yards long—unable to get out during the bombardment, they were killed by the score. A few bombs flung down the shaft and— *voilà tout*. And so they are hauled out one at a time. More holes to be dug—more shell holes to be utilised. Apropos of those Hun dug-outs, a little incident in one of them revealed yet another side of Tommy's character. Truly is he a man of many parts. A few cheery sportsmen having worked manfully and well, and having earned their rest, found the dug-out they had marked as their own was occupied. It had for the time been missed in the search for Germans; that was why it was occupied. Nothing daunted, however, they piled the occupants on one side, while they peacefully went to sleep on the other. There's no doubt getting a dead German up those shafts is weary work, and they were tired. But I'd sooner have slept in the trench myself. However, that is by the way.

And so we go on, wandering in perfect safety over the ground that a few days before meant certain death. A mass of rifles, kit, bandoliers, accoutrements litters the ground, save where it has already been collected and sorted into heaps. Unexploded bombs lie everywhere, clips of ammunition, bayonets. All has to be collected and sent back—another phase of clearing the battlefield.

Then there is the road where some transport was caught topping the rise. There the holes have to be bigger, for the horses have to be buried even as the men. It is only rarely the process is already done. One horse there was, in a trench on his back, fifty yards from the road, stone dead. How he got there, Heaven knows. He wasn't much trouble.

Then there was another mound from which protruded an arm, in German uniform, with its fingers pointing. And the hand was black.

A morbid sight, a sight one will never forget. Vividest of all in my mind remains the impression of a German skeleton, near the edge of our own trench. Dead for nearly a year perhaps, shot in some night attack, trying to cut the wire. A skeleton hand from which the wire-cutters had long since fallen, crumbled on a strand, a skull grinned at the sky, a uniform mouldered,

That, and the blackness of Death. No peaceful drifting across the Divide, but blackness and distortion.

Thus the aftermath : the price. . . .

Printed in Great Britain by Hazell, Watson & Viney, Ld.,
London and Aylesbury